The
Social System
of Science

The
Social System
of Science

NORMAN W. STORER
Harvard University

HOLT, RINEHART AND WINSTON
New York   Chicago   San Francisco   Toronto   London

Copyright © 1966 by Holt, Rinehart and Winston, Inc.
All Rights Reserved

Library of Congress Catalog Card Number: 66–18799

28179–0116

Printed in the United States of America

To my father, Professor N. Wyman Storer,
and my mother, Mary Emily House Storer

Preface

The sociology of science is a comparatively young branch of sociology, yet the healthy growth it has shown within the last few years suggests that it is not presumptuous now to concern ourselves with its conceptual integration. A field of knowledge can develop coherently only when an adequate conceptual framework is available, and while it may be premature to suggest that sociologists working in this field are already being divided into "theorists" and "experimentalists," I think it is appropriate to consider the construction of a body of assumptions within which our research findings may be most fruitfully interpreted.

This book, then, is an exercise in sociological theory-building. It attempts to develop a theory of the social organization of science. I have tried to indicate its possible broader relevance by pointing out certain basic parallels between the "social system" of science and other social systems within society. I hope, further, that the approach used—even if not the specific conclusions I have drawn from it—may be useful in bridging the gap that seems now to exist between those sociologists who are concerned with society as an entity and who analyze social behavior in terms of its consequences for society as a whole and those sociologists who are concerned first of all with the motives, attitudes, and goals of the individual participants in these patterns of social behavior. My approach hopes to answer the question of why it is that most individuals, most of the time, come to "want" to do what it is that society "needs" them to do. Only when we can answer this question satisfactorily, can we develop a sociology capable of providing both prediction and meaning.

To acknowledge all those who have contributed to my thinking, through creating the universe of discourse in which it has taken place, would be an exhaustive job. Yet those who have contributed more directly to it, in different ways and at different times, must be mentioned by name although none of them may be blamed for my own errors and shortcomings. To the following, then, I am particularly grateful: Theodore Abel, Bernard Barber, Joseph Ben-David, J. Stefan Dupre, William Evan, Henry B. Eyring, Barney G. Glaser, Gerald Gordon, Henry Guerlac, Warren O. Hagstrom, Walter Hirsch, Donald A. Kennedy, Roger G. Krohn, Simon Marcson, Robert K. Merton, Nicholas C. Mullins, Donald Pelz, Don K. Price, and Herbert A. Shepard. Finally, for their special part in stimulating and encouraging me all along the line, let me thank Charles K. Warriner, Norman and Barbara Kaplan, Robin M. Williams, Jr., and Talcott Parsons. My sincere appreciation goes also to Miss Diana Meister and Mrs. Mary-Theresa Smith for their diligent labors in typing and retyping the manuscript.

N. W. S.

Cambridge, Mass.
March 1966

Contents

The
Social System
of Science

CHAPTER *1*

The Scientific Importance of Science

Let me begin with a controversial statement. Modern science is of little or no importance to the vast majority of the world's population, including the population of advanced, industrialized nations. Whether it be viewed as a body of knowledge about natural phenomena, expressed in esoteric prose and mathematical formulae and housed in libraries, or as a set of methods for the study of these phenomena, the existence of science and its work in advancing knowledge has almost no direct effect upon the man in the street anywhere in the world.

Rather it is the application of scientific knowledge in engineering and other forms of technology that have wrought such spectacular changes in the material context of our lives over the past century, and it has been the "popularizers" rather than scientists themselves who have facilitated the impact of scientific findings upon our basic values and our view of the world. It is only because of the increasing dependence of technology on scientific progress and the closer ties between science and the common universe of discourse, that we now speak of the "practical" importance of science.

Today we do tend to lump the two together. We read statistics on "scientific and engineering manpower," and Congress debates the amount of funds to be appropriated for "research and development." We think of our achievements in space as scientific triumphs (although the failures are always "engineering failures," much to the chagrin of the engineers who were also responsible for the successes). With our usual tendency to oversimplify, we have muddied the distinction between the production of generalized knowledge and the application of this knowledge to specific problems.

Actually, it has only been within the last century, if as long as that, that scientific progress and technology have been related at all. Before that time, and in some areas to this day, technological change was almost entirely independent of progress in science. Probably the first important application of scientific knowledge to practical problems occurred in the mid-nineteenth century when aniline dyes were discovered and their manufacture formed the basis of the great German dye industry. Before that time, developments in architecture, navigation, industrial processes, and armaments had come not from scientists but from men interested in solving immediate practical problems rather than in building of a body of generalized knowledge. Later in the nineteenth century, Edison continued this tradition; his famous search for a dependable electric light filament seems to have been purely a matter of cut-and-try, guided hardly at all by reference to scientific knowledge of materials and their properties.

But it has been increasingly the case that scientific advances are directly responsible for technological advances, so there is actually increasing justification for saying that science is important in our daily lives—even though the connection is still indirect. Through the application of scientific knowledge, we now live longer and more comfortably than at any time in history, even though at the same time we may feel that we are losing some of the cherished values and patterns of behavior that have made life worthwhile. Innovations in transportation and communication, in medical practice and industrial processes, have introduced temporarily unsettling changes into people's lives almost as often as they have created new freedoms or brought welcome relief from old problems. In the broadest terms, we may say that man's increasing control of his natural environment, made possible by advances in scientific knowledge and made real by technology, has been primarily responsible for the accelerating rate of social change that we have experienced since the end of the last century.

However, if the application of scientific knowledge has improved our lives, it has also made them more precarious. Knowledge is a two-edged sword, and both edges become sharper as our store of knowledge expands. At best, the darker applications of scientific knowledge provide defenses for our country; at worst, they have made it possible for us to blow ourselves entirely off the face of the planet. As international political, and economic affairs are influenced more and more by the practical import of new scientific advances, it becomes even more important that this force in our lives be better understood.

The Study of Science

My purpose in writing this book is not to explore the influences of science upon society but to explicate the nature of science as a participant in this relationship—to determine the internal characteristics of science as a social system. For these purposes, then, we will define science not as a body of knowledge or set of investigatory techniques but as the organized social activity of men and women who are concerned with extending man's body of empirical knowledge through the use of these techniques. The relationships among these people, guided by a set of shared norms, constitute the social characteristics of science. To the extent that these patterns of behavior remain stable over an appreciable length of time, we may discuss them as components of an organized system of behavior and attempt to determine the relationships that exist among them. This is, in my view, the central purpose of the sociology of science. It is true that scholars in many fields have taken up the study of science as a social phenomenon, largely because of its obvious importance to society. Here, however, we shall undertake the analysis of the social characteristics of science because of their scientific importance—

because their analysis is of extreme importance in the extension of sociological theory.

As the title of the book indicates, science will be treated here as a social system; that is, as a complex of interrelated patterns of interaction, guided by a shared body of norms and values and influenced by the characteristics of its social environment, distinguishable from other types of social activity in society.

Just as the physical and biological scientists have found, throughout the history of science, that particular objects of study facilitate the investigation of particular phenomena because in them these phenomena may be observed with unusual ease or clarity, so the sociologist who is concerned with a particular topic will find certain aspects of society especially suited to the study of that topic. Science, as will become clear in subsequent chapters, is a relatively simple social system, one that allows us to see in bold relief certain general aspects of social systems that in the economic or political system, for example, may be obscured by their greater complexity.

In the social system of science, for instance, we do not find a complex differentiation of roles. At most, we find "junior" and "senior" scientists, whereas in the economic system we find complex and overlapping established roles such as buyer and seller, and employer and employee. The less complication of this sort a social system exhibits, the easier it will be to determine the basic structure of the relationships that constitute the system. Similarly, because science is a relatively "new" institutional component of society, its basic values are still visible: they are not taken for granted by everyone to the extent that no one bothers to state them explicitly any more. This part of society does, to be sure, engage in quite complicated relationships with other parts of society, but my concern here is to analyze the nature of science itself rather than its place in the larger society.

It is because of the theoretical importance of science, then, rather than its practical importance, that I have written this book. My long-range purpose is to see what influence the investigation of the social nature of science can have upon the extension of general sociological theory. This is not a treatise on sociological theory in the broad sense, but to the extent that my analysis of science is based on a more general concept of social systems, it will constitute something of a test of this approach to the analysis of social systems, and thus may be relevant to more general concerns. Further, if a theory can be the most practical thing in the world—and the relationship between Einstein's Special Theory of Relativity and the Manhattan Project suggests that this is sometimes true—then from this analysis may come some useful ideas concerning the basic structure of society as well as of science.

The Sociology of Science

It is a convention among sociologists to indicate their substantive area of interest by saying, "My work is in the sociology of X," meaning that they are particularly interested in the sociological analysis of X. The sociology of science is a relatively new specialization within the discipline; probably no more than a dozen sociologists claim it as their major interest now, and only within the past ten years has it gained a place on the program at sociological meetings. Yet the literature of the field is accumulating rapidly and the field seems likely to experience considerable growth in the next few years. Because this is the area of study with which this book is concerned and to which it is hoped that it may contribute, it will be valuable at this point to review briefly the history of the field and to take stock of its current status.

In listing the subdivisions of sociology, most sociologists tend to pair the sociology of science with the sociology of knowledge, a habit that indicates the framework within which they have viewed science in the past. Science has been seen primarily as a source of knowledge, as the part of society that produces new information about the empirical universe, rather than as a unique system of behavior within society. This is indeed a useful point of view, so long as one's focus of interest is society as a whole; in this perspective, it is science's contributions to this whole that are important—and its sole output to the larger society is knowledge. Defining science in this way, sociologists have asked about the social conditions under which science can most effectively perform this function, about the effects of scientific knowledge and its application upon the rest of society, and about the nature of the values of an entire society that make it possible for science to emerge as a recognizable social activity. It has been an interest in science as *deus ex machina* rather than as a phenomenon worthy of investigation in its own right that has characterized most sociological concern with science before the 1950s.

But this is not the only point of view from which to study science. We are now moving rapidly toward the investigation of science as a particular sort of social behavior, one which, for all its important relations with the rest of society, can be studied as an independent part of society rather than merely as part of a larger one. Following A. R. Hall (1963), we can say that the major landmark in the separation of the sociology of science from the sociology of knowledge came in 1938 with the publication of Robert K. Merton's "Science, Technology, and Society in Seventeenth Century England" (1938). Hall suggests that this was the last important empirical work to approach science from the perspective of the sociology of knowledge; it is significant that at the same time and thereafter, Merton was at work on a brief but critically important series of papers that were directly concerned with the social organization of science rather than with its relation to the rest of society. These papers are "Science and the Social Order" (1938), "Science and Democratic Social Structure" (1942), and "The Machine, the Worker, and the Engineer" (1947).[1] They may be said to form the main link between these two sociological perspectives on science, because they originated from Merton's study of the values of science and their relations to the larger society in which they developed, and they then went beyond this to examine the social-structural characteristics of science that must necessarily accompany these values.

In the early 1940s there also appeared Florian Znaniecki's *The Social Role of the Man of Knowledge* (1940) and Logan Wilson's *The Academic Man* (1942), neither of them strictly concerned with the sociology of science but both paying major attention to the general question of knowledge-centered roles in society. In 1952 Bernard Barber's *Science and the Social Order* was published; this book remains the only major attempt to outline the entire field of the sociology of science and to treat in some detail the broad range of topics which the field may someday be expected to cover in depth. Since that time there has been a gradual but steadily growing interest among sociologists in the topic—although, as Kaplan (1964) points out in his review of the field, the bulk of published work in the area still has tended to come from people outside the discipline of sociology.

Prior to about 1940, then, science was nearly always viewed either as an entity that might or might not develop in different social milieus, or simply as a source of information having various consequences for the rest of society. Thereafter, sociological attention has slowly shifted toward a focus on the internal organization of science. A detailed history of the field is not necessary here, but it is interesting to note that it has been suggested that this history is itself a problem of legitimate interest to the sociologist of science. Merton first made this observation in his Foreword to Barber's book (1952), and more recently, in his article on "Resistance to the Systematic Study of Multiple Discoveries in Science" (1963), he has carried the analysis forward considerably.

A survey of the current state of the field will complete our review of the body of knowledge with which this book is concerned. It should be noted first that the activities of the scientific community are often studied by social scientists today because of their contributions to technology rather than because they are of intrinsic interest as social behavior for sociological study, and that the individual scientist as well as the social organization of science is being investigated from many different points of view. The clinical psychologist and the political scientist—not to mention the economist, the sociologist, and the historian—are beginning to pay attention to the scientist as an interesting subject of study.

As yet, however, I feel that there exists no comprehensive conceptual structure that seems capable of ordering the welter of information now being published. Investigators from different disciplines are studying science in terms of their own fields' concerns, but sociologists lack a general framework within which these findings may be integrated. My work here is addressed to this problem; it is an attempt to extend the current "theory of science," not through a series of specific propositions but through generalized description of the patterns of interaction that characterize science and of the forces that maintain them. Before proceeding, it will be valuable to see what approaches to the study of scientific activity have been taken and what materials are already at hand. These materials may be divided, more or less conveniently, into seven categories.

1. *Science as a social institution.* From this perspective science is viewed as a system of social behavior, complete with norms, values, demographic characteristics, and organizational forms, as well as a definite history. The works of Barber (1952, 1956a, 1956b), Hagstrom (1965), Krohn (1960), Kuhn (1962), Merton (1938, 1957b, 1961, 1963a, 1963b), Derek Price (1963), Shepard (1956), and Storer (1961, 1962a, 1962b) are illustrations of this approach.

2. *Scientists as members of concrete groups.* Problems of morale, group influences upon productivity, recruitment, and the management of research have been the major foci of work in this area. Contributions here have come from Barnes (1960), Benis (1956a, 1956b, 1956c), Brown (1954), Glaser (1964), Kaplan (1959b, 1963), Marcson (1960a), Pelz (1953, 1956, 1959, 1962), Perry (1963), Shepard (1956), and Storer (1961, 1962a).

3. *Scientists as members of a profession.* This approach differs from that which sees science as a social institution, in that it views science not as a self-contained social system but as a corps of experts in interaction with other parts of society. Such studies have concentrated on the growth of professional organizations, the training of scientists to assume professional roles, and the problems involved in the relations between scientists and the rest of society. This approach is represented in the work of Kornhauser (1962) and Strauss and Rainwater (1963), and is prominent also in that of Barber (1952), Ben-David (1960a, 1960b), Bello (1954), Glaser (1964), Knapp and Greenbaum (1953), Marcson (1960a, 1960b), Merz (1961), and West (1960a).

4. *Scientists as creative individuals.* Studies in the psychology of scientists may be divided between those concentrating on the origins and general personality characteristics of people who become scientists, and those analyzing the nature of scientific creativity itself. In the former area contributions have come from Eiduson (1962), Cooley (1963), Kubie (1954), Knapp and Goodrich (1952), Roe (1953), and West (1960b). In the latter area we may cite such works as those by Taylor (1963), Stein and Heinze (1960), and Coler (1963).

5. *Scientists as members of specific disciplines.* There have

been a few studies that concentrate on members of specific disciplines, such as those of chemists by Strauss and Rainwater (1963), of physiologists by Meltzer (1956), of medical researchers by Kaplan (1959), and of mathematicians by Collette (1963). Such studies have, however, tended to concentrate upon one aspect or another of the discipline rather than to make the specific nature of the discipline an important variable itself. For an initial attempt to assess the consequences of differences among disciplines according to the type of knowledge with which they are concerned, see Parsons and Storer (1966).

6. *Science as an influential participant in national decision-making.* Since Sputnik I went up in late 1957, the relations between science and government have become a major focus of interest. Among works that have taken this approach to science are those of Dupree (1957), Dupre and Lakoff (1962), Gilpin (1962), Gilpin and Wright (1964), Lamson (1960), Don K. Price (1962), and Wolfle (1959). Studies of science and government in other countries have come from Ben-David (1962), Dedijer (1957, 1961, 1962), DeWitt (1960, 1961, 1962), and Kaplan (1962).

7. *Science as a communication system.* This has been perhaps a narrower approach to science than those mentioned above, but it has been particularly promising because it focuses directly upon the dynamics of the bloodstream of science. Garfield (1963), Garvey (1963), Gordon and Marquis (1962), Menzel (1958), and Shilling (1963, 1964) have made important contributions here.

This listing of important materials in the investigation of science is by no means exhaustive; for a more complete review of the literature, the reader is referred to Barber (1956), Kaplan (1964), and to Barber and Hirsch (1962). It may, however, indicate to the reader what is happening now in the social-scientific study of science, and how recent most of the literature is. A great deal more information about scientists, their attitudes towards their work, and their behavior in different situations, is certain to be produced in the near future. It is imperative that progress also be made in providing a theoretical framework within which each new contribution to our knowledge of science may acquire richer meaning and more general relevance to the concerns of sociology. The present volume represents an attempt to provide such a framework.

The Plan of the Book

The analysis of science to be presented here is based upon a general model of "social systems," their basic characteristics and dynamics. My use of the concept differs somewhat from that of Parsons (1951) and of Loomis (1960), and after a discussion in Chapter 2 of the major questions now confronting the sociology of science, Chapter 3 is devoted to a discussion of this central concept. In it I try to establish the epistemological background of the basic model and to show through describing the major institutions of society—the political, economic, family, and religious institutions—as social systems that the concept has general relevance to the concerns of sociology.

Chapter 4 discusses the sociological context of creativity and how the creative urge is adapted to social structure. Because the desire to be creative is taken as the basic source of "energy" in the social system of science, this topic is crucial to the argument that science may actually be analyzed as a social system.

Chapter 5 describes the social system of science itself, showing how the values of science and the central importance to scientists of *priority* in discovery—both described first by Merton—can be seen to fit the general model of social systems developed previously. The analysis is pursued in Chapter 6 through an examination of a number of the "social problems" of science, suggesting that the model is adequate, although not "proven," to the extent that it helps explain the nature of these problems.

Finally, Chapter 7 is concerned with the future of this social system. The major trends that characterize science and its position in society today are assessed for their probable impact upon the social and normative structure of science within the next few decades, and an attempt is made to predict the major social characteristics of American science at the end of this century.

Footnote for Chapter 1

1. These papers are all to be found in Merton, *Social Theory and Social Structure* (Rev. ed., New York: Free Press, 1957), pp. 537–573.

CHAPTER 2

The Sociological Analysis of Science

A theory is a generalized, systematic, and economical description of the relationships that exist among a number of facts or data found within a delimited area of empirical phenomena. It may also be an "explanation" of the phenomena, because "how?" and "why?" blend into one another so imperceptibly. If one is satisfied to know that *A* causes *B*, and does not ask how *A* comes about, the proposition *explains* the relationship; if one is also concerned with the appearance of *A*, however, the statement, "*A* leads to *B*" is merely a description. One criterion of a scientific theory, then, is whether it gives one a sense of closure or of satisfaction that the "why?" has been answered as well as the "how?". This book may be said to have originated in my feeling that the current "theory of science" does not answer enough "why's?" to be satisfactory. Hence, these introductory words about the nature of theory.

The principal criterion of good theory is usually considered to be the theory's predictive power. If a theory is adequate (and it may be better to use this word than "good" or "correct," for several theories may all be able to predict the same phenomena equally well), it will yield predictions that are correct within the range of variation considered necessary by the person who is checking them against the facts. In the end, of course, the theory yielding the most correct predictions will be preferred, although this is not the only criterion of adequate theory. Two other considerations play a part in the evaluation of a theory.

First are the related criteria of economy and generality: the theory that can explain the widest range of phenomena most concisely is the most general and economical. The matter of the theory's "elegance"—its aesthetic qualities—may also be a consideration here, although it is not directly relevant to the scientific adequacy of the theory.

Second, there is the matter of how well the theory affords opportunity for logical transition to other theories, either those concerning "adjacent" phenomena or those which are more comprehensive and concern data at other levels of generality than those covered by this theory. Here, the better theory is the one that extends our powers of explanation; it provides leverage in understanding other types of phenomena and it supports or shows the way toward refining broader theory.

Related to this criterion is that of its capacity to generate meaningful new questions. In one sense this criterion is irrelevant to the evaluation of the immediate adequacy of the theory to explain data now at hand, but because science strives continually to explain more phenomena, a theory that does pose new questions is potentially capable of explaining more data and of possessing greater power of generalization.

In the sociological analysis of large-scale social phenomena (macro-sociology, as it is called), opportunities for testing predictions are quite limited—partly because it is impossible to carry out "experiments" on large numbers of people in real life, and partly because change usually takes place so slowly in real life that we do not have the patience to wait upon the data that might test a prediction. For these reasons, sociological theory must be evaluated more frequently in terms of the other criteria described. We do make use of "natural experiments," of course—

finding natural instances of the interaction of the variables we are particularly interested in, rather than producing these instances ourselves—whenever we compare different groups or societies; however, the difficulties involved in partialing out all factors but those whose relationship is being tested, as well as in being sure that our identification of the factors makes valid comparison of the two cases indeed possible, mean that even here it is extremely difficult to make decisive tests of predictions.

Because the sociologist is thus limited in his opportunities to make direct tests of his predictions, he must evaluate his theory more in terms of its apparent economy and generality. Does it seem to make sense of the data we now have? Does it stand in a determinate and fruitful relationship to other theories? Does it suggest new directions for research? These must be the criteria we employ throughout this book as we attempt to improve upon current sociological analyses of science.

Science as a Focus of Sociological Analysis

The sociological study of science is a type of macro-sociology, and is in the usual position of a relatively new subfield of any discipline. It has more facts than it has theory to explain them. Facts about science—its demographic characteristics, its financial support, the personalities of scientists, and the folkways and mores of science—are becoming plentiful. As yet, however, I am not satisfied that we have done a fully adequate job of making sense of these facts. This is not to say that there is no theory at all available at present, or that what there is is incorrect, but that I do not believe it to be fully satisfactory in terms of the criteria I have outlined above. The theory that will be developed here must be seen essentially as an attempt to expand upon the existing analyses of science, and as such will be indebted to them for having laid the foundations of the entire enterprise.

The important thing is that a sound, comprehensive theory of the social organization of science be established, so that our understanding of it may be more complete and that we may bring its analysis into a cogent relationship with other sociological theory. In this sense, incidentally, the analysis of science may be viewed as a natural experiment, in that the pinpointing of what makes science different from other types of social activity, and why, may enable us some day to test certain propositions that derive from more general theory.

It is impossible to study something without a framework of assumptions to guide one's work. Facts never "speak for themselves," but acquire meaning and significance only within such a framework. Because we shall view science as a social structure—a complex of statuses or social positions whose particular relationships are recognizably independent of other relationships in society —we must consider it as a self-sustaining entity. We may view it as a subsystem of society, a structure that is not fully autonomous but yet may be distinguished from other parts of society. Science is an occupation in which men and women engage, and its central characteristic is that it involves specialized knowledge. The framework of assumptions founded upon the concept of "profession" is thus an appropriate one to use in our approach to the analysis of science. What do we know about science as a profession?

First of all, we know that there are today in this country about a quarter of a million people who may, on some grounds or other, be classified as scientists. Science is essentially the name of an activity in which people are engaged, and, as with other "principal occupations," the definition of who is "in" it must necessarily be somewhat vague. We may view the core, or central cadre, of science as being composed of those individuals who participate most completely in this activity, with a series of other groups lying at various distances from this core and containing those people who participate less in this activity.

Ideally, the scientist is an individual who spends his working day in basic research and related activities: gathering information, reporting his findings, evaluating the work of other scientists, and so forth. He is engaged directly in the attempt to extend our generalized knowledge of some aspect of the empirical universe. There are probably very few people who fit this specification completely, however, because someone who is entirely engaged in such work is unlikely to be producing something that is of such immediate value to others that his activities merit their financial support. Because such people—a few "research professors" in universities, the prestigious scientists supported by industry to do basic research entirely, and those researchers who are supported by career investigatorships—are so few, the immediately adjacent groups of persons must be included in the core group. These are composed of scientists who spend some of their time teaching in colleges and universities and those who are doing some applied as well as basic research in industry, government, and nonprofit organizations. Altogether, this group probably includes somewhere around 50,000 people in this country, in all fields of science.

Beyond this core we find those who teach but do little or no independent research, the strictly applied-research people, the part-time administrators, the independent consultants, the technicians, and the graduate students preparing to join these groups. Where one wishes to draw the line between scientist and nonscientist will depend more upon *why* one wishes to draw the line than upon there being a clearly discernable gap between the core group and adjacent groups. I shall argue here that this central cadre of scientists constitutes the principal reference group for most of the other groups—that the norms and values characterizing it serve as ideal standards for the others—and that against this ideal normative structure we may assess variations in the behavior of scientists in a variety of situations. The analysis of science to which this book is devoted, then, is assumed to be most pertinent to the central cadre of scientists, and true to a lesser extent of those who fall within the boundaries of our scientific universe but are, in operational terms, only partly scientists.

According to the National Science Foundation's *National Register of Scientific and Technical Personnel* for 1962,[1] roughly 40 percent of the 215,000 persons included in the *Register* were in industry, 30 percent were in educational institutions, and 20 percent were in governmental organizations, with the remainder divided among nonprofit organizations, independent consultants, and "other." Thirty percent of this number, or about 65,000, reported that their principal activity was research, either basic or applied; the primary activities of the other 150,000 were scattered among teaching, administration, production and inspection, and "other."

About half of these 65,000 hold the doctorate; some 45 percent of the research Ph.D.s are in industry, 33 percent are in colleges and universities, and the remainder are mostly in government and nonprofit organizations. As we might expect, though, when we take into account the type of research in which these scientists are engaged, we find that the largest proportion of our central core of scientists is located in the universities. Of the nearly 33,000 scientists engaged primarily in basic research, half are in educational institutions, whereas less than a quarter are in industry.

Even if we are generous and suppose that as many as 50,000 scientists constitute our core group, it still represents only about one fortieth of one percent of this country's population. It is not the absolute size of the group, however, that makes it theoretically important, but the systematic difference of these activities from those of other groups in the population. That these activities have a tremendous, though indirect, impact upon the lives of all of us is undeniable, but this fact is not immediately relevant to an explanation of the roots and the nature of the patterns of behavior that characterize scientists.

Science as a Profession

Basic research is the "purest" form of scientific activity, in that it is focused directly upon, in Merton's words, "the extension of certified knowledge," rather than upon the solution of practical problems. Not only, then, is science a profession, it is essentially a "non-service" profession—a profession that does not serve the needs of laymen directly. It is of course true that the knowledge developed through basic research is often extremely useful in helping men to achieve their goals, but the very existence of a distinction between basic and applied research suggests that the utility of knowledge is not its *raison d'être* so far as most scientists are concerned.

This follows from the fact that the "logic" of constructing an organized body of generalized knowledge differs from the "logic" of solving problems; in the former case, comprehensiveness and generality are the main goals, whereas in the latter they are specificity and immediate applicability. Because a researcher can rarely work according to both standards at once, there is a strong tendency to do one *or* the other, even though a scientist may engage in both types of work at different times. As Shepard (1956, p. 56) writes: "The present-day scientist who would be both 'pure' and 'applied' can be likened to an actor who plays to two audiences simultaneously, each with a different taste in shows."

It is this lack of a central concern for the utility of its product that makes science a non-service profession, as distinguished from law and medicine. A brief review first, of the characteristics of professions in general, and then of science in particular, will set the stage for our discussion of the sociological theory of science as it now exists.

We may say that a profession has four major characteristics. First is its responsibility for a body of specialized knowledge —responsibility for its maintenance, transmission, and extension or application. All professions are vitally interested in its maintenance and transmission, but generally they must choose between emphasizing its extension or its application. The professional competence of the members of a profession must be judged in terms of their command of, and sometimes their contributions to, this body of knowledge. Ideally, such individual characteristics as race, religion, or political opinions should be completely irrelevant to membership in a profession.

Because only other members of a profession are capable of evaluating an individual by these criteria, it follows that a profession must have autonomy in the recruitment, training, and control of its members. This is the second characteristic of a profession. To the extent that nonprofessionals are able to influence the selection of a profession's members, their training, or their behavior as professionals, the quality of their specialized knowledge and the effectiveness of its application may be undermined.

The third characteristic concerns the relation of the profession's members to the larger society. As professionals, they must establish regular relationships with the rest of society that ensure their support as well as their protection from outside interference. The service professions, particularly law and medicine, serve society directly on a "fee-for-service" basis (even though in many instances the fee is determined by a sliding scale), and are thus involved directly in the economic system. Expertise is exercised in the service of nonprofessionals in return for economic support paid either directly to the professional or through the group that employs him. A rigorous emphasis upon service and upon commitment to the best interests of the client is obviously necessary if the service professional is to retain the layman's trust, inasmuch as the opportunity to exploit one's expertise is an intrinsic aspect of the "information differential" that exists between expert and layman. Yet because the service professional is typically supported directly by nonprofessionals, his colleagues do not have the collective power to regulate the "rewards" he receives. They may control his professional reputation vis-à-vis the layman to some extent, although public criticism of a professional by a colleague is extremely infrequent and is usually condemned. To the extent that a service professional is concerned with the application of his knowledge rather than with its extension, the esteem of his colleagues must be based upon his skills rather than his contributions, and this may or may not be important to a given individual.

In the non-service professions, however, science particularly and the academic profession more generally, expertise is not "sold" to laymen in the same way that it is by the service professions. As was pointed out earlier, it is for this reason that there are so few scientists whose entire activity is devoted to basic research; the products of basic research are, almost by definition, not of immediate value to the layman, and so society is less willing to support this activity. (The fact that basic research is supported rather handsomely now by the federal government does not contradict this argument; this support is premised on the government's assumption that the products of basic research will *eventually* be of practical value, even though this possibility is not the basic researcher's goal in most cases.) To be sure, the applied scientist does sell his expertise, but the application of knowledge is not the central concern of science, and the applied scientist is in this respect somewhat removed from the "center" of the profession.

The basic scientist more frequently earns his support from society through teaching, but even this is not a "service" in the same sense as is medical care or legal advice. An education is not sought in a crisis to solve an immediate problem, and the teacher's responsibility to his students is quite different from that of a service professional to his clients. In the Kantian sense, education is a "pure pleasure," whereas medical and legal services tend more often to be perceived as "mixed pleasures"; that is, one could presumably continue to be reasonably happy without higher education, but one's situation in life might decline precipitously if medical or legal aid were not obtained at the proper time.

Closely related to the problem of a profession's relation to its environing society is its fourth characteristic, its need for a type of reward that both motivates its members' activities and may be used for purposes of control by the profession. As was pointed out above, when a professional receives such a reward—be it money or gratitude that he finds most gratifying—directly from nonprofessionals, he may be subjected to temptations to subvert the principles of his profession: for example, the doctor who performs an illegal operation, or the lawyer who induces perjury in a witness. Because this situation exists mainly in the service professions, they must depend to a greater extent upon such methods of social control as licensing or disbarrment than must the non-service professions. In the latter case, the motivation to belong to the profession is not so clearly economic, or even one of service.

Much recent work on the social organization of science has focused on the question: What is the nature of the reward that motivates scientists? This work began in the mid-fifties with Shepard's (1956) paper on "Basic Research and the Social System of Pure Science," and Merton's (1957b) Presidential Address to the American Sociological Society (now Association) on "Priorities in Scientific Discovery: A Chapter in the Sociology of Science." Because, on the one hand, the scientist is not generally in a position to be of direct service to laymen, and on the other, the economic rewards for scientific endeavor have (until recently) not been particularly attractive, the question of what scientists "get" in return for their work has been crucial to the understanding of the social dynamics of science.

It was Merton who initially brought the theoretical significance of *professional recognition* to the attention of sociologists. In his address on "Priorities in Scientific Discovery," he spoke of "the reward-system in science," and pointed out that recognition by one's colleagues that one has indeed made a valuable contribution to science is the institutionally appropriate reward that motivates scientists, even though it may not be the reward that is personally most gratifying to every individual scientist. This is truly a reward whose allocation can be controlled by one's colleagues rather than by nonprofessionals; it is directly related to the institutional goal of the advancement of knowledge; and

Merton's analysis of battles over the assignment of priority throughout the history of science shows that recognition based on priority is highly valued and continually sought.

However, despite the voluminous amount of data that Merton has brought to bear on the problem and his analysis of the social dynamics of science based upon them, I am not convinced that the question of *why* professional recognition is able to serve as the motivating reward in science has yet been adequately explained.

The Meaning of Professional Recognition

Using the sociological concept of "profession" as a framework for our analysis of the social organization of science, I have suggested that the social autonomy of science—its responsibility for a specialized body of knowledge—is basic to its continued existence in society. But autonomy means more than freedom from outside interference; it requires internal organization, the existence of ordered relationships among the members of the profession, relationships which they must somehow be motivated to support and to participate in. Simply, then, we must ask not only *what* it is that makes it worthwhile for scientists to participate in these relationships, but *why* it is worthwhile to them.

To ask *why* is to ask for an explanation rather than simply for a description. Particularly in the social sciences, it is to ask for an answer based upon facts or assumptions that we can accept without question, and this usually requires reference to feelings and motivations we have experienced ourselves. In a way, this is seeking to find the link between what we "know" personally and the things that we know more objectively—our "data." I think it is not unscientific to let this aim guide our work, because our findings must still be subject to objective, scientific scrutiny before they can be accepted.

Before we can provide an explanation, we must elaborate our description here; we must examine in more detail the nature of professional recognition. It means, first of all, the public acknowledgment by other scientists that one has made a valid and significant contribution to their body of knowledge. This may be expressed simply through their footnoting one's work—the acknowledgment that this work has been valuable in helping them to discover more about a given topic—as well as through more openly laudatory affirmations of achievement. Glaser gives a useful list of the varied forms that professional recognition may take: "eponymy, prizes, awards, fellowships, scholarships, honorary memberships and committee work in scientific organizations, editorships, honorary degrees, professorships, chairs, lectureships, consultantships, mention by historians of science, publication, acknowledgments in others' work, and evaluations by colleagues" (1964, p. 2).

As Merton has made clear, recognition must be based mainly upon priority of discovery. Inasmuch as one must be the first to announce a discovery if it is to be a "discovery" at all, battles over priority are essentially battles for professional recognition. The *second* man to arrive at a particular discovery, even if his work was entirely independent of the original discoverer, has lost virtually all opportunity for recognition and for immortality via the literature of science; the discovery will always be known as, say, "Jones' Law" rather than "Smith's Law," and because the journals are uninterested in publishing material that has already appeared elsewhere in substantially the same form, Smith must conclude either that his labors have been in vain or else that he must contest Jones' right to priority.

That such battles are often bitter and protracted may be seen in Merton's encyclopedic analysis of struggles over priority that date back to the early seventeenth century. And he rightly points out that the value of professional recognition has been institutionalized to the point that scientists not directly involved in the contest feel they have an important stake in its resolution. They may be instrumental in initiating the contest through persuading one party or the other in the dispute to press his claims; "the disinterested moral indignation," that lies behind such actions, Merton suggests, "is a signpost announcing the violation of a social norm."[2] That the scientist *should* want professional recognition, in other words, is supposedly binding upon all scientists. It is an aspect of the rights and obligations that they have accepted upon coming to occupy the social position of "scientist."

Merton (1963b, p. 270) attributes the scientist's interest

in obtaining professional recognition to his basic commitment to the goal of science, because it is through the receipt of recognition that he is assured he is living up to the requirements of his profession. "In general, the need to have accomplishment recognized, which for the scientist means that his knowing peers judge his work worth the while, is the result of deep devotion to the advancement of knowledge as an ultimate value." In his address of 1957 to the Americal Sociological Association, Merton spelled this out in more detail:

> Recognition of what one has accomplished is thus largely a motive derived from institutional emphases. Recognition for originality becomes socially validated testimony that one has successfully lived up to the most exacting requirements of one's role as a scientist. The self-image of the individual scientist will also depend greatly on the appraisals by his scientific peers of the extent to which he has lived up to this exacting and crucially important aspect of his role.[3]

Yet Merton also points to the ambivalence of scientists about professional recognition. Based on a good deal of evidence from, among other sources, the letters and autobiographies of scientists, his suggestion is that this ambivalence has led scientists to ignore the frequency of multiple discoveries as a topic of scientific interest in itself:

> This resistance to the study of multiples and priorities can be conceived as a resultant of intense forces pressing for public recognition of scientific accomplishments that are held in check by countervailing forces, inherent in the social role of scientists, which press for the modest acknowledgment of limitations, if not for downright humility. Such resistance is a sign of malintegration of the social institution of science which incorporates potentially incompatible values: among them, the value set upon originality, which leads scientists to want their priority to be recognized and the value set upon due humility, which leads them to insist on how little they have in fact been able to accomplish . . . the tension between these

kindred values creates an inner conflict among men of science who have internalized both of them. Among other things, the tension generates a distinct resistance to the systematic study of multiples and often associated conflicts over priority.[4]

While the scientist is supposed to want professional recognition, then, he is also supposed to deny this interest. So again, then, an aspect of the behavior of scientists is interpreted as an indirect consequence of commitment to the goal of science. The question of ambivalence will be viewed from a new perspective in Chapter 6.

Just as the goal of science, which the scientist either already had when he came into science or was trained to accept, gives meaning to professional recognition, so too it underlies the scientist's commitment to the norms of science—the specifications of how he ought to behave as a scientist. These will be discussed in more detail in Chapter 5; here we will treat them only in a general sense. Merton writes: "The institutional imperatives [of science] derive from the goals and the methods. The entire structure of technical and moral norms implements the final objective."[5] Stressing the development of the autonomy of these norms, he continues: "The mores of science possess a methodologic rationale but they are binding, not only because they are precedurally efficient, but because they are believed right and good. They are moral as well as technical prescriptions."[6] Once established, then, apparently on the basis of their functional relationship to the goal of science, the norms assume a life of their own and become "right and good" as lesser but still absolute values.

It is thus the goal of science that, according to Merton's analysis, shaped the social structure of science. It provides the standards by which successful role-performance is assessed, and the implicit codification of behavior considered necessary to the achievement of this goal comprises the norms of science. This view has, of course, been further elaborated in Merton's own work, and, most directly, in the work of his student, Barney S. Glaser. It has provided guidance for research in several directions. Glaser (1964 and 1965), for instance, has examined the relationship between the receipt of "adequate recognition" and scientists' morale under varying conditions, and between commitment to the goal of science and prior socialization.[7]

In the later of these works, Glaser suggests that "The degree to which a scientist will be motivated to advance knowledge varies positively with the degree colleagues involved in his training and work experience advocate this as his major occupational goal to the exclusion of other goals."[8] The data he presents in support of this proposition, however, seems to me to be open to question on two counts. First, Glaser does not provide information to help us decide which of his variables ("high experience," having received doctoral training and having taught or done research at a university, and "high motivation," answering positively questions about the importance of freedom in research and about wanting to contribute to basic scientific knowledge) came first. Glaser seems to imply that "high experience" came first and then led to "higher motivation," but he also opens the door to the alternative interpretation when he writes, "In choosing science, the scientists may indicate a readiness to internalize the goal both quickly and to a high degree. Perhaps to justify their selection, these scientists become highly motivated to advance knowledge within a short time."[9] At best, the question cannot be answered on the basis of the data Glaser presents.

A second question, unanswered altogether, is that of why the scientists originally came to science. If it were not because of an interest in advancing knowledge, then there must be some real discontinuity between personal motivation and institutional motivation, and this is difficult to accept when Glaser's introductory remarks read in part, "Research performance, unlike many other kinds of work, cannot be enforced. Rather, it must come as a product of the enthusiasm that an individual feels toward his work. A key factor, then, in accounting for the quality of work of scientists is their degree of motivation to advance knowledge, the main institutional goal of science."[10] I, at least, find it difficult to assume that such a central motivation in a man's life must come primarily from what he has been taught after the age of eighteen.

The same explanation of scientists' motivation appears in Hagstrom's book, *The Scientific Community* (1965), probably the best available discussion of scientists' folkways and mores. Hagstrom writes, "The socialization of scientists tends to produce persons who are so strongly committed to the central values of science that they unthinkingly accept them. . . . These commitments are the outcome of a prolonged training process, lasting well into adult life, in which the student is effectively isolated from competing vocational and intellectual interests and in which he is extremely dependent on his teachers."[11]

My concern here is that no attention is paid to what originally attracted the students to a career in science. That such motivation, originating outside of the scientific community, must be important can be seen in Hagstrom's statement, ". . . only fractions of those interested are permitted to graduate in the exact sciences and enroll in graduate school. Attrition in graduate school tends to be high, and only the more competent and highly motivated students obtain the doctorate. Among those who do obtain doctorates in science, only a fraction are permitted to enter careers in basic research . . ."[12] Hagstrom's emphasis here is upon the system that does the selecting, not on the individual's desire to be selected, and he continues to suggest that the "highly individualistic view" of scientists as "self-starting" and "self-controlling" is "incomplete."[13]

By the same token, however, I think a theory that does not take account of the individual's initial motivation to enter science is incomplete. *Given* the institutional goal of science, *then* socialization to this goal can occur and *then* the norms of science, describing the patterns of behavior necessary for its achievement, can develop. But we need yet an explanation of where this goal originated and of what it is about certain individuals that makes them particularly willing to enter the arduous socialization process that we call scientific training.

In line with this problem is the question of explaining instances of concern for priority *before* the middle of the eighteenth century, the period during which the scientific community is assumed to have been established. Merton (1961, p. 483) mentions some thirty-six multiple discoveries (discoveries made or independently claimed by two or more individuals) prior to 1700, over which priority disputes arose in thirty-three cases. He cites Galileo's complaints about others' attempts to "rob me of the glory which was mine," and Bacon's warning that "it is enough to check the growth of science, that efforts and labors in this field go unrewarded. . . . And it is nothing strange if a thing not held in honor does not prosper."[14] There must have been something about priority that was of personal, as well as institutional, value to Galileo; and Bacon must have had some sense of the importance of professional recognition to researchers even before their roles were normatively defined.

I am suggesting that the personal as well as the institutional meaning of professional recognition must be examined if we are to develop a more comprehensive theoretical analysis of the social dynamics of science. For instance, if the motivational importance of professional recognition lies in its affirmation of successful role-performance, why is it not merited even when an individual has not made an important discovery? Simply obeying the rules of the game, contributing to the general well-being of the community through supporting the norms, would seem to be "successful role-performance." The fact that it has been proposed, unsuccessfully, from time to time, that recognition be allocated on the basis of these criteria as well as of the criterion of discovery (for instance, in the suggestion by the editor of *Science* that scientists should receive their colleagues' acclaim for writing review articles as well as for significant discoveries) indicates that role performance per se may not be what is really involved.

Another question is that of why professional recognition must be public—must be recorded in the form of footnotes and prizes, and so on—rather than private. Why cannot a scientist feel adequately rewarded for successful role-performance by the verbal praise of his colleagues, rather than insist that it be recorded for posterity in the literature and through eponymy? There is an important but unrecognized distinction, I think, between wanting the approbation of one's peers in a general sense—wishing them to approve of one's role-performance—and the desire to have one's scientific accomplishments recorded "permanently."

Toward a More Comprehensive Theory of Science

It is on the basis of these questions, unanswered so far as I can see by the current sociological view of science, that I think there is room for improvement in current analysis of the social dynamics of science. This improvement must be twofold: First, it must take into account the psychological foundations of the reward-system in science, and second, it must establish firmer links with general sociological theory. Although this improvement will involve some reinterpretation of the relationships among the components of the present theory, it will not entail a refutation of any of the main points established by Merton and those working along the lines he has laid out. Rather, it is hoped that the current sociological analysis of science will be deepened, and that the fundamental value of Merton's work will be placed in even clearer perspective.

I shall attempt this expansion (1) through a redefinition of professional recognition so that its relationship to scholarly creativity may be seen in a new light, and (2) through demonstrating that science may be viewed not only as a profession but also as a "social system," comparable in basic dynamics to other social systems, so that a sociological theory of science may be systematically related to sociological investigation of other sectors of society. This will involve first a consideration of the general concept of social system, then an analysis of the social components of creativity, and then the proposal that the dynamics of science are essentially the same as those of the economic, political, family, and religious social systems within society. Finally, there will be a discussion of how certain important problems of science may be understood in these terms. I shall conclude with some remarks on the future of science as a social system in American society.

Footnotes for Chapter 2

1. National Science Foundation, *American Science Manpower, 1962*, NSF 64–16. (Washington, D.C.: Government Printing Office, 1964).
2. Merton, "Priorities in Scientific Discovery," quoted from Barber and Hirsch, eds., *The Sociology of Science* (New York: Free Press, 1962), pp. 447–85.
3. Merton, "Priorities in Scientific Discovery," pp. 454–455.
4. Merton, "Resistance to the Systematic Study of Multiple Discoveries in Science," p. 250.
5. Merton, *Social Theory and Social Structure*, p. 552.
6. Merton, *Social Theory and Social Structure*, pp. 552–553.
7. Barney S. Glaser, " 'Differential Association' and the Institutional Motivation of Scientists," *Administrative Science Quarterly*, vol. 10, no. 1 (June 1965), pp. 82–97.
8. Glaser, " 'Differential Association'," p. 95.

9. Glaser, " 'Differential Association'," p. 90.
10. Glaser, " 'Differential Association'," p. 82.
11. Warren O. Hagstrom, *The Scientific Community* (New York: Basic Books, 1965), p. 9.
12. Hagstrom, p. 11.
13. Hagstrom, p. 11.
14. Merton, "Priorities in Scientific Discovery," p. 458.

CHAPTER **3**

The Idea
of Social
System

The Concept of System

If we are to understand science as a social system, we
must first get a more general idea of what is meant by "social
system." Let us begin with the abstract concept of "system" itself.
A system is defined by Floyd Allport as

> Any recognizably delimited aggregate of dynamic elements
> that are in some way interconnected and interdependent
> and that continue to operate together according to cer-
> tain laws and in such a way as to produce some charac-
> teristic total effect.[1]

There is more to this definition than may initially meet
the eye; it concerns the most basic act in any science: observation.

The words *recognizably* and *effect* are our cues. They remind us that anything we observe and identify in the world, be it natural or social, may be defined as a system, for it is producing some "characteristic total effect" upon us. Its effect may be direct or indirect, but if it did not produce such a "total effect," we would not bother to name it, for there would be nothing to name, so far as we are concerned.

In this sense, a football game is a system, a birdcall is a system, even a rock is a system. The interaction or interdependence of the system's parts may range from being almost purely spatial, as in the case of the rock's component molecules or the elements of a picture, to almost purely temporal relationships, as in the case of the bird's song or spoken language. The football game has elements of both dimensions and is thus more complex; it has both spatial characteristics (the boundaries of the field) and temporal aspects (the sequence of plays, the allotted playing time).

Not only must these elements have regularly patterned interrelationships, but their relationships must be distinguishable from those that exist in the system's surroundings. Things that participate in these relationships are members of the system, whereas the ones that do not so participate must lie outside its boundaries.

What can we say in more detail about the patterns of interaction—that is, interrelationships involving cause and effect and occurring over time—that make up a system? First of all, we can say that these patterns must be such that the elements making up the system will be able to repeat them. This is true in principle, regardless of how much time may elapse between repetitions of particular acts or patterns of acts. Those patterns that cannot or will not be repeated are either not essential to the identity (the boundaries) of the system, or else failure to repeat them at the "proper" time will result in a lessening of the system's distinction from its surroundings, if not in its dissolution. Because the events or acts that constitute *systemness* are interdependent, one following regularly upon another in one or more interwoven cycles, failure on the part of one member of the system to play its part will tend to disrupt the patterns that constitute the system.

We may say also that these patterns of interaction need not be directly obvious to an observer. Much of the work of science involves the discovery of such systems as well as the tracing out of the patterns of interaction within identified systems. There are many systems, both organic and mechanical, which have easily identifiable boundaries (for example, plants, animals, automobiles, rivers), but there are many which are too large, or occur over too long a span of time, to be immediately apparent. In these cases, it is only when particular patterns of interaction have been followed out until we find them forming regular cycles that we have some inkling that we have discovered a new system.

Finally, we may say that all systems are abstract. They are constructions of the observer's mind as much as they are "real," for any given physical object is simultaneously a participant in many systems and in the long run its actions can never be predicted on the basis of only one or two of its system-memberships. A tree, for instance, participates in an ecological system, a gravitational system, perhaps in an agricultural system, and so on. Knowing its place in the ecological system will not enable us to predict its sudden destruction in a forest fire, and knowing its place in the gravitational system will not help us to know when it will be chopped down as timber.

We are so used to thinking of these systems abstractly, or in isolation from other systems, saying "all other things being constant, this is what will happen," that we sometimes fail to realize that the description of a system is not actually a description of reality. It is a *partial* description of reality only: this *caveat* will be particularly important to remember when we discuss social systems.

A system, then, is our identification of a group of interdependent relationships in the "real world," a group that continues to exist ("produce some total characteristic effect" upon us) over time and that if fully understood and isolated from other intersecting systems would be absolutely predictable. It is because we cannot describe all of reality at the same time that we must deal with these "parts of reality," even though such an approach cannot yield absolutely valid predictions. To be sure, we can often isolate one system from others for periods of time long enough to make it worthwhile—a radio, a car's motor, a package of frozen food, a skyscraper: these are all "systems" that we have created and that are useful to us because we, too, are systems which exist only for a limited time. Scientific laws, however, are established on the assumption that the passage of time will not affect their validity and so they must describe parts of reality rather than all of reality at once.

With these assumptions in mind, we may now discuss social systems.

The Dynamics of Social Systems

Social systems are a special class of systems, for as Parsons (1937), pointed out some 25 years ago, a social system is a *voluntaristic* system. That is, we grant the premise of free will to the participants in the system, if only because of the myriad of different goals they seem to be seeking, and assume that through various processes they come to *want* to engage in some patterns of interaction, and to avoid other patterns.

Parsons states in his fundamental paradigm of interaction, which is important here:

> An established state of a social system is a process of complementary interaction of two or more individual actors in which each conforms with the expectations of the other(s) in such a way that alter's reactions to ego's actions are positive sanctions which serve to reinforce his given need-dispositions and thus to fulfill his given expectations.[2]

To paraphrase, Parsons is saying that the patterns of interaction among two or more participants in a social system are maintained because the reaction of the participants to one another's behavior is mutually rewarding. Implied here is the assumption that each participant has some standards by which to judge whether the other's actions are appropriate or not, and also that the other participant knows of these standards so that he can choose the behavior that will elicit rewarding behavior from the first.

Assuming the existence of such shared standards, we may turn our attention to the problem of specifying what we mean by "rewarding behavior." Obviously we cannot restrict this concept to the relatively simple matter of someone's smiling at us or saying "Good for you!" We are perhaps misled by the common-sense meaning of "rewarding," in that it calls to mind a sensation of unexpected pleasure or of something gratifying beyond what we had initially expected. The term as it is used here shall refer to all behavior that fulfils one's expectations. (The question of whether the little boy who expects a spanking in return for some misbehavior finds his expectations "rewarded" when his father comes home, is a neat one, but one not crucial at this point.) To avoid such irrelevant connotations, the term *commodity* will be used hereafter in place of reward.

Parenthetically, it should be remarked here that the use of an "exchange model" in the analysis of social behavior is by no means new in sociology, although it has experienced a revival in the last ten or fifteen years. For more extended, and somewhat different, treatments of the topic, the reader is referred to Homans (1958), Gouldner (1959), Kuhn (1963), and Blau (1964).

There is an infinite number of things Alter can do that will be gratifying to Ego, of course, but we must assume that these can be subsumed under a manageable number of categories. As a rough approximation to these categories, we may list the following: (1) Alter can transfer physical objects to Ego's possession; (2) he can affirm Ego's beliefs about himself or something else; (3) he can act at Ego's suggestion; and (4) he can share himself with Ego in various ways. The most fundamental of these exchanges is the last, especially in the matter of sex; the bisexuality of species represents the original division of labor (no pun!) within a species, and thereby sets the stage for an exchange-relationship. As the division of labor (the differentiation of action-systems) proceeds, the other categories become important as areas in which exchange-relationships will develop.

To look at the other side of the coin, it becomes obvious that large-scale and relatively stable patterns of interaction can be established only when there is a widespread trust that many Alters want and will continue to want a given kind of commodity. Expectations of Alter's behavior, cued to certain situations and shared widely among people, can develop only when Ego is assured

that he will be able to elicit the behavior he desires from Alter—
and that Alter will have a vested interest in the kind of behavior
that Ego can exhibit.

At this point, it will be useful to consider the basis upon
which this sort of trust develops, for this is necessary if we are
to understand why violations of trust, or of expectations, are
frequently greeted with punitive countermeasures. If there is any
rationality in man at all, it seems naive to assume that all negative
sanctions are administered out of the primitive feeling of aggres-
sion that frustration seems to produce. After all, the milk *is* spilt:
chastising the child will not put it back in the cup.

To begin with, we must turn Kant's famous "Categorical
Imperative" around backwards. This was his particular formula-
tion of the Golden Rule: Perform every act as though it would
immediately be written into universal law and thereafter determine the actions of everyone else. We rarely guide our own behavior on this basis, to be sure. But we *do* view others' actions
in this light—we treat their acts not only as specific acts but
also as *precedents*. We chastise the child "So you won't do that
again," and his immediate protest is, "I'm sorry, I won't do it
again." He is asking us *not* to view his action as *setting a precedent*.

Because we tend to look at others' actions in this way,
we soon shift from considering the empirical *likelihood* that they
will continue to behave this way to a consideration simply of the
principle involved. We no longer concern ourselves with the probability but with the possibility. And we think not only of the
possibility that a given individual will repeat an action but that
his act may set a precedent for others. In the realm of unspecified
probability, a single violation of an expectation assumes considerable importance. It threatens *in principle* the reliability of our
expectations, and to maintain this reliability we try to ensure that
the violation will not be repeated with any frequency.

There is of course wide variation among people in terms
of how likely they are to see a specific act as threatening a principle (bureaucrats are noted for this ability), but in general we
may assume that this kind of thinking does play a large role in
our everyday responses to the actions of others.

Even when there is universal trust among individuals that
most people will usually be interested in obtaining what they have

to offer, simple and relatively clear-cut means to determine *who is interested in obtaining what* must be available. The determining criteria may be the inherent characteristics of the individual (for example, age and sex); they may reside in the situation ("If ya don't wanna buy somethin', why'd ya come in the store?"); or they may be related to time (few, if any, restaurants offer beef-steak dinners in the morning). Beyond these major, impersonal means, of course, Ego must often specify what it is he wants before Alter can know how to respond.

Within each of these categories, however, there are large numbers of individuals; therefore, it is reasonable to develop general expectations about what sort of behavior is appropriate to elicit a desired sort of complementary behavior. In other words, stable exchange relationships can develop only around those commodities in which there is widespread and relatively continuous interest.

As each different type of commodity comes to be identified separately, there develops a corresponding need to develop patterns of shared expectations concerning how one may obtain it. People come to have a vested interest in knowing where, when, and how they may obtain something they want, whether it be sexual gratification, the coordination of the actions of others, or material goods. And there thus develop not only ideas about how to get something from Alter, but also sentiments that he should be corrected when he does not fulfil these expectations.

To sum up: The process of structural differentiation, or the progressive division of labor, means in one sense that patterns of interaction through which different commodities may be obtained become more and more clearly distinguished. For example, no longer do we expect a woman to make her husband's clothes; the emphasis now is more heavily upon her role as a companion, both sexual and social, than upon her economic functions. Accompanying this "division of expectations" is an implicit interest in maintaining these distinctions. Given the relative immediacy of most human needs, and at the same time the fact that our needs are not always in phase with those of others, there develops a need to trust that people will be willing to participate in an exchange with us when *we* want to, even if they may not feel a complementary need so strongly at the same time.

Various mechanisms (called "generalized media" by Parsons[3] have been developed to solve these problems. This involves the development of symbolic media that retain their value over time and thus serve to cancel out the problem of coordinating people's needs in terms of time. Money is, of course, the outstanding example. Another such mechanism, important when what is needed involves the actions of another individual rather than a material good, is that of assigning responsibility for a certain type of action to a certain person or group of persons; the marriage vows ensure for the husband, among other things that a source of sexual gratification will be available when he wants it (and, conversely, it ensures the same thing for the wife, together with a reliable source of support). Similarly, the principle of tenure of office, whether hereditary or elective, means that we need not seek leadership on an *ad hoc* basis whenever the group requires it.

It must be kept in mind that the description of a social system is not intended to be an empirically precise description of social behavior, but a description of the basic framework of expectations that serve to coordinate interaction among people and according to which they evaluate each other's behavior. In this sense, a social system is an "ideal type" based on the ideal set of norms that people share and thus it has consequences for their behavior, even though it is not a complete or entirely accurate description of all they do. Yet such an ideal type must be generally descriptive of real behavior, for if people disregarded it altogether they would cease to find it a useful guide to interaction and would soon forget it.

To clarify the origins of any social system and the means by which it is maintained, we must turn to what might be called *the principle* of "the principle of the thing." I refer to the assumption that people's mutual definitions of appropriate behavior may be traced back to their ideas about what actions would or would not, if carried out regularly by everyone, threaten to destroy the fabric of the relationships in which they are engaged and through which they are able to satisfy their needs. We are always carrying out thought experiments, first asking ourselves, "What will happen if this goes on?" and then behaving in relation to what we think is likely to happen in the future. Social norms seem to be mainly descriptions of the patterns of behavior that only a few people think will lead to undesirable consequences, and that are thus acceptable to nearly everyone.

The covert violation of these norms by a few people may not be too important, but our expectations of what would happen if everyone *explicitly* denounced them are important in determining how we respond to violations of them. We do, after all, have a vested interest in how most people ought to act, even if we and our friends violate certain norms regularly, for we must often interact with people whom we cannot trust to know the informally established rules that enable *us* to violate these norms without confusion. Much of the advantage we gain through violating norms comes from the fact that others obey them; cheating is advantageous only when most other people do not cheat.

So the norms must be upheld "in public," and it is at this point that the basic rules or norms that governing a social system come into contact with the real behavior of individuals. To uphold them means that we must occasionally punish behavior that violates these norms, just as the formal laws of a society are upheld by the police and the courts. To fail to do this, or in effect to deny their rightness, would undermine the common culture that contains these norms and that enables strangers, people who have no established private mutual expectations, to interact effectively. As society becomes more complex and the frequency of interaction among strangers increases, the importance of publicly supporting the common culture of a social system also increases.

When a social system contains more participants than can possibly know each other personally, it must have an ideal set of norms against which the behavior of both friends and strangers can be measured (although, again, we are often prepared to tolerate violations of these norms by people with whom we have worked out alternative sets of expectations). Still, the existence of the basic norms is assumed, and we are always prepared to return to them if and when other expectations fail.

It is for this reason that the ideal of how participants in a social system should behave is of fundamental concern to the sociologist, even if in fact relatively few people follow the ideal literally. And it is for this reason that a model of the social system of science is important even if it does not describe with complete accuracy the behavior of all scientists. Falling bodies rarely accelerate at exactly 32.10 feet per second per second, yet without this abstract law we should find it almost impossible to make sense of the behavior of falling bodies in differing circumstances.

The Principles of Exchange in Social Systems

Postponing for the moment consideration of the fact that different types of commodities require different patterns of exchange, I propose that for any large-scale, stable pattern of interrelationships that has developed around the exchange of a particular commodity, there are three basic principles that must be supported if the participants' trust in the system is to be maintained.

The first of these is that the participants in the exchange-system must *want* the commodity in question. It is only when Ego has faith that Alter will want what he has to offer that he will voluntarily interact with him. This may be no more than the assumption that Alter will respond to a courteous request for information, in return for some indication of gratitude, or it may be Ego's unspoken assumption that Alter will be glad to take his money in return for some object that Alter possesses. The point is not that Ego has some personal knowledge of Alter's wants but that he defines Alter as being subject to this principle, sometimes simply because Alter is a human being but more often because Alter is defined as a member of the same society or more specialized group. The obligation resting upon Alter is to try to respond to an offer of "fair" exchange, or else to explain why he is not interested at the moment in obtaining the commodity that Ego has to offer.

The second principle is that the commodity must be obtained *through exchange with others*. Whereas three of the four major commodities must necessarily be acquired through interaction with others, they might be obtained through the use of force or fraud rather than through fair exchange.[4] Even in the case of material goods, many of which might be privately produced for one's own consumption, there are subtle pressures to obtain these through exchange with others. The basic idea here is that people apparently want to belong to a group (which may be an entire society) in which individuals are interdependent, because this promotes increased efficiency through the division of labor, among other things. This is the general case of the importance of "vested interests"; we usually define this as the merchant's wanting me to buy from him rather than produce for myself because he "needs the business," but his vested interest is really the outcome of his having acted previously on the assumption that others will want what he has available for exchange.

The third principle is that individuals must *not compromise different exchange systems*; that is, they must not employ the behavior appropriate to obtaining one commodity in order to obtain a different one. To do so—for instance, to exchange money for power—would be to "dedifferentiate" the exchange-systems and to make it more difficult for Ego to know how to go about getting what he wants from Alter.

If any of these three principles are violated, Ego's motivation to continue interacting with Alter will be weakened, for he can no longer be so certain of Alter's willingness to respond "appropriately" to what he has to offer. We find, then, that as Ego sees Alter tending to violate any of these principles, not to speak of his directly violating Ego's expectations concerning their immediate interaction, Ego will tend to respond negatively to him. He will invoke punitive measures or he will try to withhold *other* commodities in which Alter seems to be interested, inasmuch as Alter has already shown himself to be uninterested in obtaining through appropriate behavior the commodity that Ego had to offer originally. This is the simple process of saying, in effect, "If you won't give me what *I* want, I won't give you what *you* want."

If our reasoning here is correct, we would expect to find norms in any major exchange system—which from this point on I shall call a "social system"—that seem intended to support these basic principles. We should find, in other words, that the norms of a social system center around the support and protection of the integrity of that system's "native commodity."

I intend eventually to propose that science has its own native commodity and that its dynamics can be explained in terms of the general model outlined above. For the moment, however, let us look at the major social systems of society in an attempt to illustrate in more detail the principles and processes that have been outlined thus far.

The Major Social Systems of Society

THE ECONOMIC SYSTEM

The concern with obtaining the basic necessities of life has been a dominant theme throughout human history. Briefly, it has progressed through three stages, the last being itself of very remote origin. The mythical isolated cave man was responsible for the entire problem of feeding, clothing, and housing himself and only rarely entered into any lasting exchange relationships with others, except perhaps with a cave *woman*. As soon as groups were established, however, there must have developed a crude barter-system in which, for example, a hunter would exchange part of his kill for a pot, or for a basket of berries; in this way he could use his time more efficiently and at the same time obtain a more varied diet.

A "pure" barter system, however, is also difficult to imagine as existing for very long in an expanding group. The problem of coordinating needs would be too great to allow this, particularly in the case of perishable items like meat. A developing group apparently has two major directions in which it can go at this point; the first is to develop a kind of generalized trust that one's contributions to the group will be compensated in the long run by the benefits one receives from it. Mauss' work on gifts (1954) develops this alternative considerably.[5] The other alternative is to develop concrete symbols of generalized value; here, interaction involving the possession of objects will involve the immediate exchange of things. Although such a development may appear to be less desirable for group cohesion because there is less dependence upon mutual trust, it apparently is necessary if the economic system is to become more sharply differentiated from other types of exchange later on.

Here, general symbols of value, perhaps originally non-perishable items of real utility such as tanned skins, pots, weapons, or even nuts, would come to act as a crude form of money. A man might acquire, say, as many stone knives as he could, not because he wanted to use them all but because they would not turn rotten and could thus be used in barter at any time. And as soon as others began to see knives in the same light, they would be pleased to acquire them because of their value for trading rather than for their specific utility. Decorative items, probably because they were relatively small and even less likely to be "used up," probably became the chief items used in "money barter," or what we might call "generalized barter."

Although this "prehistory" of the development of money is naturally speculative and is intended really to illustrate the *meaning* of the economy as an exchange-system, there is some evidence to bear it out—we do know that such items as wampum, golden ornaments, and jewels were used very early in history as symbols of wealth.

One belt of wampum was not exchanged for another, however, but for something that the individual needed, something he wished to consume or use for himself. The interchange thus consisted of an exchange of "money" in return for something specific; the seller would then be able to "spend" this money in turn for something specific that he needed. We may assume that, very gradually, patterns of expectations, sometimes embodied in explicit laws, developed around this sort of exchange. They had the main effect of enforcing the contract, or the terms of the exchange, between Ego and Alter, so that each could trust the other not to cheat him or to rob him after the exchange was completed. With the further elaboration of the economic system, in particular the development of capitalism where the temporary "purchase" of money itself became central, more norms were developed to keep these more elaborate exchange-patterns stable.[6]

The economic social system may thus be identified as the complex of statuses or social positions whose interrelations are concerned with the exchange of money for goods or services, with the money circulating in one direction and goods or services in the opposite direction.[7]

Harking back to our three necessary constraints, let us see how they are embodied in this particular social system, the economic social system, today.

The principle that a participant in this system must continue to *want* to acquire the commodity is difficult to identify as an explicit law or requirement; it is too fundamental to rise to this level of objective awareness. A good way to see it in action, however, is to watch the reaction of someone whose money is refused by someone whom he has reasonably defined as the potential seller of something he wants. The popular saying, "Every man has his price," suggests that all people are desirous of acquiring money. Moreover there are some laws on the books that make it mandatory for a person to sell his wares—whether they be clothing, food, entertainment, or lodging—to anyone who has the required amount of money. Fair Housing laws embody this principle, as do the recent Civil Rights laws concerning hotels, restaurants, and recreational facilities. Only in cases where there is presumed to be a particular danger to a particular class of people are exceptions made to this principle. Cigarettes and liquor are not sold to persons under a specified age, nor are they allowed to attend certain types of entertainment. But ask a teen-ager how he feels when he is refused a pack of cigarettes: "I've got the money, why won't they sell it to me?" Exceptions to the principle that "legal tender" must be accepted when offered in exchange for an item or service that is normally for sale are acceptable only if they can be justified by a set of higher or more important values.

The principle that one must not create this commodity for himself, but rather acquire it through legitimate interaction with others, is embodied in our laws against robbery and counterfeiting. Even the creation of goods and services for oneself will after a certain point be disapproved of by others: merchants would object if all people made their own clothes or produced all of their own food, and there are local laws prohibiting people from installing plumbing or wiring in their own homes. If one were to generate either money or goods and services for oneself, he would no longer be sensitive to the needs of others—he would no longer have an interest in fulfilling their needs in return for what they have to offer—and such a situation cannot be tolerated in principle, even if no particular individual is deprived of anything specific.

The outrage felt by the victim of a thief and the threat to the very existence of the monetary system by the excessive production of money, are parts of the same picture. To lose one's money, or the goods one has purchased with one's money, is not only a personal loss but is seen as eventually threatening the principle that money is valuable and desirable. Money would become less valuable if robbery were to become an everyday experience or if everyone had more than he needed; and if one cannot obtain full value for the money one has acquired, why try to get it in the first place? The problems of inflation and deflation are considerably more complex, but from this point of view, they are ultimately related to the individual's trust in the continued interest of other people in obtaining money.

A discussion of the third principle, concerning what makes illicit the compromising of different exchange-systems, must wait until we have discussed the other major social systems of society.

THE POLITICAL SYSTEM

The issue of power, that is, the use of physical force as a mode of interaction between people, became apparent as soon as there were two hungry cavemen who both had their eyes on the same piece of meat. In small groups of men, then, just as we see today in flocks of chickens, there must have developed what we would call a pecking order—a rank-ordering of individuals determined in the same way that professional baseball or football teams are ranked today—according to who can beat whom.

The number of individuals who can be so rank-ordered, however, is relatively small. In a group of, say, more than thirty men, all jostling for better position, it would be nearly impossible for one man to keep track of with just which individuals he had better share his food and which individuals he could safely rob. It may have been this sort of uncertainty, where neither of two men could be sure he could win in physical combat with the other, that led to the first idea of barter; in such an exchange, physical supremacy did not need to be tested because each party came away from the interaction relatively satisfied.

However, the need to coordinate the actions of several men in a group, and the occasional necessity of dealing with other groups of men, kept the problem of power important. If a continuing series of contests to keep the pecking-order straight was impossible, and if the coordination of collective action was occasionally needed, some other means of determining leadership became necessary. How this was worked out in different groups and at different times probably varied tremendously, and yet in groups that became larger and more powerful, we can assume that a form of leadership must have been institutionalized and that a means of determining who was the leader came to be agreed upon. Groups that did not develop such a social mechanism sooner or later would have dispersed or been incorporated into other groups that did have such a mechanism.

For a group to be successful, in other words, stable leadership is a necessity. If a group cannot determine whom to look to for direction when the occasion warrants it, or if its members are unable to cooperate in relatively long-range activities because there are no agreed-upon criteria for selecting its leaders, the group cannot succeed very well in such long-term undertakings. Yet the fact of leadership, of being really able to direct some of the activities of others, carries with it certain material, as well as psychological, benefits—and it would be unlikely that only one man at a time would desire to be a leader. But an uncontrolled struggle over the occupancy of such a position would reduce the group to a pecking-order society again in a very short time. The *means of acquiring* a position of leadership, therefore, had to be standardized; and, having attained this position, its occupant had to be assured somehow that he would not be deposed the very next day.

Some of the benefits accruing to the leader were sharable, and a very important way of maintaining one's position was to exchange these benefits for support. The sharing of spoils by the war-leader with his supporters, the distribution of tribute among them, and the bestowal of choice lands and other rights upon them, served to secure his position. He made further use of his supporters in suppressing rebellious elements within the group, while his chief supporters each tried to gather supporters of their own in order to help them retain the favor of the leader.

Although such tactics have not changed over the years, certain refinements have developed that differentiate more clearly the political system, for this is what I have been describing, from the economic system. It is not clear exactly how this came about, but we may speculate that two factors had a great deal to do with it. One was that as the group increased in size, the leader (be he emperor, king, sultan, pharaoh, tsar, or sachem) came to depend more upon his supporters for material assistance than they upon him. To support an army, to maintain the civil servants who had to engage on a full-time basis in administering the laws and in other state activities, and even merely to display the symbols of leadership was costly. An income more dependable than the spoils of war was needed, and this could be acquired only through the help of the leader's supporters.

Related to this is the second factor. Because supporters must have varied in the amount of support they could help him acquire, the problem of maintaining order among his supporters was often crucial for the leader. One way to avoid competition and disruption among them was for the leader to resist dealing out the rewards he had to give solely on the basis of who provided the greatest assistance in obtaining economic support. Thus this political necessity also weakened the spoils system. Finally, weakening of the spoils system combined with the fact that as the population grew the leader's position depended more and more upon the consent of the people (to control them by force would require much greater effort), pressures must have mounted to make a separation between economic wealth and political influence. The leader needed support for his policies, many of which would not by their very nature yield material that could be used to reward his supporters, and so the appropriate reward for support came more and more to be that of having a voice in policy decisions. Frequently, of course, these decisions had a direct effect upon the supporter's opportunities for economic gain, but the direct connection between wealth and power had to be broken, at least in principle if not always in actual practice.

The terms of the political exchange thus came to be *support* in return for *influence,* or conversely, a hand in *policy decisions* in return for *loyalty.* In the same way that money became a generalized medium, useful in the purchase of any item, so loyalty had to become a generalized commitment; it meant *general* support of the leader in his policies, in return for the opportunity to influence those policies of particular interest to the individual supporter.[8]

In the political system, as in the economic system, the norms encouraging participation in this exchange-system are almost so deeply rooted as to be unavailable for objective examination. Perhaps it is more a fact of life than a moral imperative that one must participate in this exchange-system if one wishes to affect another's actions, that one must support the leader's policies generally if one is to have a chance to influence the direction that these policies take.

The rules against exercising power on one's own are to

be found in the laws against the employment of force in one's dealings with others. To rob a man at gunpoint is to arrogate to oneself the power to direct his behavior (the handing over of the wallet) without his consent and without there being any exchange involved, and the precedent that this seems to set—that one man's direction of the actions of others is not subject to any control on their part—is in principle a threat to the exchange-system that has been established to regulate the use of power among men. The laws against peonage in this country focus more directly upon this problem than do those against robbery; peonage involves the exchange of more than material goods and money—forced servitude.

To be sure, certain areas of social life are partially exempted from these general rules. The father does have certain powers of coercion over the members of his family, particularly in his right to discipline his children, but even here the political system imposes restraints upon the extent to which this power may be legitimately exercised. Cruel treatment of children is defined as the use of power beyond the limits that society sets upon the private control of force. Although physical altercations between men are tolerated up to a point, a charge of disorderly conduct often means that a man has been apprehended while personally employing more force than that which can legally be exercised by a private individual.

We have already discussed in part the origin of norms prohibiting the use of economic rewards to "purchase" political rewards, but this matter will be dealt with at greater length after we have discussed the other two major social systems of society.

THE FAMILY SYSTEM

It is not really contradicting the fact that sexual relations can be one of man's highest and most ennobling experiences to say that the need for such relations is primitive. Mankind was endowed with this need before it ever recognized its humanity; that it has become the vehicle for something beyond mere momentary sensation is a product of this humanity, but it does not mean that the human relationships based upon it are not rooted in extremely basic urges.

The cooperation of two persons required to satisfy this

need is perhaps the basis of the exchange-system we refer to as the family system. To the extent that man desires a predictable world, that he wishes to plan ahead so that he may satisfy future sexual needs, an enduring relationship with someone of the opposite sex is the optimal solution.

Something more than a mutual exchange of sexual favors is necessary to establish such a continuing relationship. For one thing, regardless of our present knowledge that this need may be as strong in the female as it is in the male, the purely biological differences between male and female mean that the relationship cannot be exactly symmetrical in either sexual or social terms.[9]

The most important of these differences is pregnancy, which in the later months may seriously hamper a woman's ability to be self-sufficient. These biological differences, together with the likelihood that sexual relations have a tendency to bring out particularistic emotions (*this* man or *this* woman becomes the object of a great amount of interest, rather than *any* man or woman), mean that a more complicated arrangement than the simple exchange of sexual gratification is necessary to establish a continuing relationship.

We may speculate, on the basis of this reasoning, that the exchange basic to the marriage relationship involves the provision of exclusive sexual access on the part of the woman in return for material support and protection on the part of the man. In this way, if we assume people to be reasonably rational in the long run about their needs, both the woman's need for economic support during pregnancy and for protection against those males who would use her for sexual gratification without providing anything in return, and the man's need for a reliable source of gratification and for other material services, are simultaneously satisfied in the marriage arrangement.[10]

This is not to say that a multitude of other factors does not also enter into the situation, or that a multitude of various patterns of arrangement is not possible, but simply that this constitutes the basic exchange involved in what we call marriage. It is possible that the woman may receive her support from her mate's brother, or that in certain circumstances she will share her mate with other women. Because the family was for millenia the basic economic and political unit of society, this exchange relationship became intricately entwined with these other exchange systems. Only in highly complex societies, those in which the major exchange-systems are rather highly differentiated, do the basic terms of the marriage relationship become really clear.

The family system differs from the economic and the political systems in that the commodities exchanged within one family are not exchanged also with the members of other families. We do not find a lengthy chain of interchanges here, but a vast series of independent systems. Yet although the actual details of the relationship differ from family to family, the *principle* of the relationship continues to be of importance to the members of all family groups in a society, and so we find strong pressures to maintain the autonomy of such systems.

Up to this point, we have spoken almost exclusively of the marriage relationship itself, and indirectly of the children that issue from it. But what of the kinship part of this system—the grandparents, uncles, cousins, nieces, and grandchildren? In our society, sexual relations between either of the marriage partners and any of these is taboo as it is, with some variations in the details, in every other society we know. Yet the relationships among all of these social positions often have a quality, not found in other relationships in society, that we associate with the marriage relationship.

I would suggest that these relationships are important partly because they represent what might be called extended chains of affection, but perhaps more so because they are a carry-over from situations in which blood relationships were of considerable importance in the economic and political systems.

This involves the material support of children and of other relatives (sometimes through the exercise of power to help them acquire advantageous economic or political positions) and certainly the handling of inheritances. There is also the solidarity of the extended family—the knowledge that its members will continue to be intimately associated in the future—that puts special pressure on the members to "get along" with and if necessary to help each other, thus making the family a social group in which an extra amount of trust is usually present and loyalty is usually invested; this enables them to engage in "nonsynchronized" exchanges of various sorts in which, for example, something is freely given with the expectation only that *sometime* it will be repaid. It is this sort of exchange to which Mauss (1954) has paid particular attention.

Viewing the typical American "isolated nuclear family," however, it is clear that there is nothing inherent in the biological relationship between a man and his cousin that means the patterns of interaction between them will inevitably be of a different quality than those between unrelated individuals. The same holds for a man's relationships with his grandparents, uncles, and the rest—even, in some cases, with his parents. To the extent that such biological ties facilitate economic, political, and even religious exchanges, however, the extended kinship system will continue to be of importance in human life.

The kinship system, then, although related to the marriage relationship, may be considered an adjunct to the man-wife-child group, and its importance seems to vary with the ways in which it facilitates exchange in other social systems. It is not an essential part of the basic exchange relationships of marriage.

Let us now consider how the basic principles governing all social systems are represented in the family system. We can say, first of all, that although it is not expressly legislated that men and women should want sexual gratification, we do find laws that seem to assume this. For instance, we find in many cities and states public welfare laws that definitely imply that a woman should look first to a particular man for material support—and that this should be provided in return for sexual gratification. When "incompatibility" is cited as grounds for divorce, it seems most frequently to refer to a lack of sexual gratification experienced by one or both partners, and even the requirement that the husband pay alimony seems to imply that the wife has "kept her end of the bargain" while the husband failed to keep his.

Thus, our laws and expectations support the notion that men and women should want to join in these two-member exchange systems we call marriages. Granting the nearly universal interest of people in doing just this, and granting also our general concern that such a value be supported in the behavior of others, we actually find more liberal concern with protecting the rights of those who do *not* want to get married than with aiding those who do wish to get married. The problem of homosexual relationships based on mutual consent between adults is a case in point.

Another indication of our conviction that people should want to be married is to be found in our covert attempts to help our bachelor and spinster friends find suitable mates.

This latter problem, particularly that of the unmarried woman, merges into the problem of self-generated rewards. Certainly adult masturbation and relations with animals are illegal—although, of course, almost impossible to detect and deal with—but even the fact that a woman can be materially self-sufficient seems to go against certain obscure but deeply-held principles. The bachelor, single girl, or spinster, even the young widow or widower, is looked upon with a tinge of suspicion because he or she is not participating in the normal exchange-relationship of marriage. We may say they are "not normal" if they do not seem to *want* to participate in such a relationship, and if they satisfy their needs outside of marriage, we look upon them as threatening the principles upon which the relationship is based.

To conclude: Although the evidence may not be so clear as it was in the case of the economic and political systems, we may say that one potentially fruitful way to look at and to understand the workings of the family sector of society is to see it also as a distinctive type of exchange system.

THE RELIGIOUS SYSTEM

The roots of man's continuing interest in religious matters —his search for answers to the ultimate questions of life and death, good and evil—may be said to lie in the nature of his ability to ask questions that require such answers. It takes a level of intelligence well above that of any non-humans we know to be capable of *thinking* of questions at this level of generality and significance. This is not to say that these questions are not valid, but that being aware of them (or actually creating them) depends upon the ability to think complexly, that is, to command a complex set of symbols that are logically interrelated and to identify inconsistencies among these symbols or to sense "gaps" in their coverage of important phenomena.

In other words, we ask such questions only when two conditions are present: when we find a place where an answer would replace a "blank space" in our picture of the world, and when this blank space is important to us. I think a case can be made that the life-death problem and the good-evil problem are ultimately both aspects of a crucial area of life where answers are not empirically available, although which of these aspects a society or a religion chooses to emphasize will have consequences of considerable importance for the belief system and social organization of that group.

The point I want to make is that the asking of religious questions may well originate in situations of cognitive dissonance and lack of closure, and that in the absence of empirically-demonstrable answers, human beings will seek support for the answers they have found in the agreement of others that their answers are indeed valid. Religion is thus essentially a social phenomenon; the individual who does not communicate with others about his religious questions and anwers is without effect upon the beliefs of his fellows, and thus does not influence their religious practices. If all of us were like this, we should have no identifiable area called "religion" to study.

It is true that a small proportion of people seem to be able to find satisfactory answers to religious questions entirely by themselves; for most of us, however, religion must be based in shared experience, because part of its value seems to lie in the knowledge that others are occupied with the same questions and share similar feelings about them. At minimum, this contention is supported by the almost universal existence in human societies of collective activities that are focused upon matters of life and death and of good and evil. In relatively less complex societies, of course, such activities are often woven together with family activities or with political activities, or even with economic activities. For, after all, it is not an easy task to draw a line between the abstract consideration of good and evil and the concrete recognition that a poor crop is "evil" or that success in battle is "good."

But in its pure form, religion is the collective activity that seeks to provide for its participants some sort of reliable answers to the most fundamental questions in life and meaningful support and solace in the inevitable crises which mark human existence. Perhaps its most enduring characteristic is not in the particular answers it provides but in the fact that its continuity depends upon the collective participation and affirmation of its tenets by groups of people. It is true that religion may fulfill a number of other functions, all the way from legitimating the political system and the dominant criteria of stratification in a society to providing cathartic release from personal tensions, but inasmuch as most of these functions perhaps could be assumed by other types of groups, we can assert that social system of religion is essentially the social framework within which non-empirical answers (answers that cannot be empirically validated) to crucial questions of widespread concern are given the support of the group.

To determine how this fits into our conceptual scheme of exchange systems we must identify what people exchange that is unique to the religious system. It is probably something like collectively validated answers that is sought in return for acceptance of the group's total complex of beliefs and practices. To put it more simply, it may often be "salvation" that is sought in return for worship, or "peace of mind" in return for "self-discipline." The terms of the exchange given here are of course greatly simplified and perhaps exaggerated, yet in many of the sociological discussions of religion they may be seen as providing the implicit framework within which the topic is analyzed.[11]

This sort of exchange differs markedly from those discussed previously, inasmuch as there is no exchange of material items or rights (except secondarily, in certain rituals); the exchange occurs primarily on the plane of ideas and emotions, mediated by actions that symbolize the acceptance of these ideas and emotions. While this makes the problem of assessing what constitutes "fair" exchange in religion much more difficult, it does mean that there is a "need" for the religious body to assign to someone the task of representing the group's interests vis-à-vis its individual members. Although this need cannot be said to *account* for the existence of the priest, I think we may say that the major responsibility of his position is to enforce standards of behavior based on the group's beliefs. His "enforcement" may entail only stating generally the nature of these standards but even by so doing he provides for the others a standard of comparison; actually, however, most priests are more directly concerned with the behavior of their fellow religionists: They hear confessions; they will admonish deviant members; they may at certain times lead holy wars against dissidents and unbelievers.

But in addition to the priest, the entire group can see and

judge the actions of its members and can employ informal sanctions to enforce certain important patterns of behavior. In the most extreme case, the group may deny its "commodity" to the individual who persists in violating the group's standards. An example of this, of course, is excommunication. On the other hand, particularly in a free society, the individual may withdraw his support of the group—his allegiance to its dogma and standards of behavior—if he does not feel that he is gaining the satisfaction he wants from it.

There is exchange, then, at the heart of the social organization of religion. And, as in the other social systems we have considered, there are norms important to the maintenance of this system. Obviously, the individual is encouraged to participate, occasionally on pain of death. The very existence of a non-participant is in principle a threat to the validity of the commodity that the members of a religious group are seeking, and so both proselitizing and severe sanctioning of those who fall away from the group are found quite frequently.

In most societies today where the idea of "religious freedom" is highly valued, only symbolic negative sanctions for the dissident are possible; anything else is illegal. Excommunication is of course legal, but for those who leave the church voluntarily it is, for obvious reasons, ineffective. Further, it seems that the very existence of religious freedom poses a threat to most religious groups, for by definition the entire community is unlikely to support the practices of a given church; therefore, the principle, as well as the possibility, that one may find satisfaction in another church is apparent to all. Without the overwhelming support of the community for one church, then, the individual is much less likely to be totally committed to a particular set of religious beliefs and practices.

Nevertheless, we have elevated the idea of being religious itself to a kind of good and are often content to urge simply that our fellows attend *some* church or synagogue. Presumably, the basic orientations of the various religions if not their specific details have enough in common, to allow the general concept of a community of believers to exist and to be in itself a source of some satisfaction to many. It is often more difficult to be an avowed atheist in a community than to be a member of a minority religious group.

The irreligiosity associated with large cities is probably due mainly to the anonymity of urban life; because city dwellers are apt to know only a small proportion of that urban population, the feeling of community pressure, or of the expectation by others generally, to participate in a religious group, is considerably diminished. Where church membership becomes also a symbol of status, of course, other pressures such as the need to establish one's social class may easily be substituted that encourage one to "attend the church or synagogue of his choice."

Thus, we have norms that encourage us to seek the "religious commodity," however it may be defined. And typically, there are norms also that seem to discourage us from trying to be religious in an individual and noninstitutional way, from trying to find our answers entirely by ourselves. To the extent that ritual, including attendance at services, is an important part of religious activities, it necessarily calls for patterned interaction with others. Through such participation, it seems, one's own standing in relation to the values embodied in the group's beliefs (that is, one's idea of his own fate) is confirmed by the fact that others are aware of it. The confessional and the sacraments are patterns of interaction whereby one receives direct or indirect assurance that he is capable of and perhaps close to salvation—the ultimate proof of the validity of one's beliefs.

But the individual who seems to create or to generate his own salvation appears suspect to the other members of the religious group. He is obviously a nonparticipant in the group's activities, and, just as other religious groups are in principle a threat to the validity of this group's answers, so the individual who privately provides his own answers is a threat. The stylites and the ascetics of the Middle Ages could be seen obviously to be doing something so difficult in their varied practices of self-deprivation that there could be little question that they were "paying" for their salvation, and thus they did not contradict the principle that an exchange was involved. It is true, however, that such excesses by religious hermits and other isolates were of concern to the Church, and the idea of the monastery was promoted as a more acceptable means by which an individual could, through self-deprivation (but now in groups and with a definite relationship to the organized church), express his religious feelings. That the monasteries to a large extent came to replace the practice of isolated "worship" of this type seems to show again that self-generated rewards in the religious systems come to be seen as undesirable, just as they are in the other systems we have discussed.

Maintaining the Distinctions between Social Systems

Thus far, I have tried to make a case for seeing these four major areas of social activity as distinct exchange-systems. But only half the case has been presented, the one showing that each system has its own type of reward, which it tries to keep circulating. The other half of the argument concerns the ways in which these systems maintain their autonomy through discouraging the use of each other's rewards in their own exchange relationships.

Seen in the perspective of the preceding discussion, it seems to make more sense now to know that we have informal and formal prohibitions against obtaining political power through the use of money, against acquiring money through the exercise of political influence, against the purchase of religious salvation with money (the sale of indulgences is frowned upon, and it is supposed to be no easier to "get what you pay for" in this sort of transaction than it would be to maneuver a camel through the eye of a needle), and so on. The use of force to obtain sexual gratification is severely punished in all modern societies, and prostitution—the exchange of sexual access for money—may be seen also as a violation of the principle that sexual access should be exchanged for the guarantee of generalized support and the conference of status.

The obvious fact that these prohibitions are frequently and systematically violated may then be seen as something to be explained rather than as a fact which should be built into our basic model. Just as falling bodies do not accelerate at precisely 32.10 feet per second per second, so the general principles I have suggested here are not to be found operating perfectly in "real life." But it is only after we have established an abstract model which temporarily disregards extrinsic factors, such as the effect of air-resistance on a falling body, that we may go back and begin to see these discrepancies as meaningful deviations from a theoretical baseline. We need not go into the general implications of this position; we can now proceed to a more detailed examination of creativity, which I shall propose forms the basis of the exchange system around which the social system of science is organized.

Footnotes for *Chapter 3*

1. Floyd H. Allport, *Theories of Perception and the Concept of Structure* (New York: Wiley, 1955), p. 469.
2. Talcott Parsons, *The Social System* (New York: Free Press, 1951), pp. 204–205.
3. See Talcott Parsons, "On the Concept of Influence," *Public Opinion Quarterly*, vol. 27 (Spring 1964), especially pp. 38–51, and his "On the Concept of Power," *Proceedings of the American Philosophical Society*, vol. 107, no. 3 (1963), pp. 232–262.
4. The concept of "fair exchange," focusing upon the *quantitative* aspects of exchange, has been given much more attention recently than have the qualitative differences between various types of exchange; see particularly Homans, "Social Behavior as Exchange," and Gouldner, "Reciprocity and Autonomy in Functional Theory."
5. See also Hagstrom, pp. 12–13.
6. For an extended history and analysis of the development of the economic system, the reader is referred to Robert L. Heilbroner, *The Making of Economic Society* (Englewood Cliffs, N.J.: Prentice-Hall, 1962).
7. For a more complete discussion of the pattern of "dual circulation," see Parsons, "On the Concept of Power."
8. This conceptualization draws heavily upon Parsons, "On the Concept of Power."
9. For an extended discussion of these factors, see William J. Goode, *The Family*, "Foundations of Modern Sociology Series" (Englewood Cliffs, N.J.: Prentice-Hall, 1964), especially pp. 11–18.
10. Kingsley Davis offers a similar definition of the marriage relationship; see his chapter on "Prostitution" in Robert K. Merton and Robert A. Nisbet, eds., *Contemporary Social Problems* (New York: Harcourt, 1961), p. 265.
11. This of course came originally from Emile Durkheim, *The Elementary Forms of the Religious Life,* transl., J. W. Swain (New York: Collier Books, Crowell Collier and Macmillan, Inc., 1961).

CHAPTER 4

Creativity from a Sociological Standpoint

If we are going to demonstrate that science can be seen as a social system, comparable in basic dynamics to the social systems described in the previous chapter, we must focus first on the elements that constitute its unique exchange-system. In this chapter I shall argue that the desire to be creative (a term to be defined later in this chapter) is at the base of the exchange-system operating within science, and more particularly, that the creative person has an urge, which is both natural and reinforced through training, to share his creations with others. In brief, I will suggest that sharing one's creative product with others, in return for their response to it, is at the heart of exchange within science.

This is not to say that scientists are motivated entirely by the desire to be creative, or even that all of them are necessarily partly so motivated, but that it is a scientific ideal and that the normative structure of science is oriented toward this ideal rather than toward a description of empirical reality. The desire to extend our understanding of the workings of the universe, in other words, is the baseline against which other motives must be compared. Men may actually "do" science for a variety of reasons—because it confers prestige on them, or offers them a living, in fact often a genial style of life, or allows them to remain at a desirable location—but it is creativity that is the institutionalized purpose of the scientist.

It is because the norms and values of science, which must be at the same time a common denominator for behavior and a means for distinguishing science from other professions, do center upon creativity that we may assume for purposes of sociological analysis a widespread desire among scientists to be creative. In other words, there is a "level of reality" based upon what men say, as well as a level of reality based on what they do, because others react at least as often to what men say as to what men do. Any other motive for engaging in scientific research besides the desire to be creative could be equally well served through an entirely different career, and thus other motives are not intrinsically related to the structure of science as creativity seems to be. So long as the interaction among scientists places a premium upon creativity, we may assume that they tend—while in the role of the scientist—to accept this as their major professional goal. The importance of creativity is, in effect, built into their universe of discourse; in order even to converse as a scientist, one must implicitly accept this goal.

Here we have a simple relationship between a psychological need and a set of norms and values, with their conjunction leading to a situation in which it may be fairly assumed that a central component of the scientist's role is the desire to be creative, even in isolation many scientists might deny that this is a strong motive for them. Yet if these norms and values were not also supported by the private, personal motives of those who become scientists, they would be more likely to change over time. It is difficult to believe that the normative structure of science could continue, as a completely independent causal factor, to inspire in scientists the desire to be creative when, apart from their scientific roles or without anchorage in scientists' private psychological needs, none of them felt such a desire.

There must be, then, a fairly widespread motivation to be creative on the part of those individuals who become scientists, even before this motivation is shaped and channeled by the social system of science. I propose here to discuss the nature of this motivation and to demonstrate how it becomes involved in stable patterns of interaction.

Creativity: Process and Product[1]

Creativity is usually defined as a psychological process, something that occurs within an individual's mind, and thus it has been the psychologist rather than the sociologist who has been mainly interested in it. Psychologists have examined the personality characteristics associated with varying degrees of creativity, the psychological dynamics that appear to underlie creative activity, and they have studied the personal backgrounds and the social circumstances that produce and encourage creativity in the individual.

But because creativity is a concept that has "social currency," that plays a part in the social behavior of people, it is also of interest to the sociologist. If the creative process itself is not of direct concern to the sociologist, its products certainly are. The end result of the creative process is a product—material, symbolic, or some combination of the two—that influences the behavior of others besides the creator; it has social as well as psychological reality. There is of course an intimate connection between process and product, for the latter embodies the ideas developed in the former, but this is not a necessary connection. It is possible that the process will produce something that no one else will define as creative, or conversely, that a product may be defined as a genuine creation by others when its producer neither intended to be creative nor recognizes the creativity which others find in his product.

The former situation might be illustrated by a very bad poem which may well have been produced by psychological processes quite similar to the ones that produced Shakespeare's sonnets, notwithstanding the audience's reaction. An extreme case of the latter is found in the rare instance when an abstract painting by a chimpanzee, submitted under pseudonym, wins a prize at an exhibition. The standards by which both the chimp's picture and a landscape by Cezanne are judged to be esthetically pleasing, may not be obvious either.

Yet the individual process of creativity and the social definition of creativity must be linked in some way, else there would be a totally random relationship between the creator and his audience. If such a random relationship existed, then presumably success as a scientist or an artist would be entirely a function of the amount of physical and mental effort put forth, and the creative person would never know whether he had in fact been "creative." We may assume, in other words, that the creative individual works in relation to a set of standards that exist apart from the creative process and that are essentially social rather than psychological.

The raw drive to create, then, existing within the individual, must somehow be guided by these social standards before the individual can be said to be recognizably creative. It may even be wrong to think of a native drive to *create*, inasmuch as by implication this term must make reference to the individual's social context as well as to his basic psychological dynamics. Yet, unless we wish to ignore the question of the persistence of people's attempts to produce creative products, we must posit some sort of urge toward creativity within the individual that can be molded by standards that are socially determined. We have much evidence that creativity is pleasurable, that many people seek this pleasure over long periods of time, even when unsuccessful, and that they seek others' opinions in order to evaluate their success. It is the problem of the origins of creativity that we must address before we may go on to discuss the place of creativity in social systems.

The Origins of Creativity

The idea of "effectance motivation," as developed by Robert W. White, provides a useful starting point in seeking the origins of creativity. White suggests that effectance motivation, the organism's persistent interest in novelty and in the attainment of competence in mastering it, underlies curiosity and is the central motivation in much of what we call play. This drive seems to be composed of neurophysiological and cognitive needs so that it represents in effect a partially emergent drive; its strength is based upon the interrelations between what is physiologically given and the neurophysiological processes facilitated by this structure. This point requires some clarification.

The brain as a physical mechanism seems to require a continual variety of sensory inputs. For whatever reason this may be, it is clear that the organism will purposefully seek a certain amount of novelty in its daily existence. A feeling of boredom is the usual sign that this need is not being satisfied, although this state is by no means at one extreme end of a continuum which has "interest in variety" at the other end. This extreme end is defined more clearly in experiments on sensory deprivation where the subject's contact with the outside world is severely limited through blindfolds and swathing in soft cloth, while the pure chaos of the battlefield is closer to the opposite extreme. My point is simply that human beings and other higher organisms need a mixture of order and novelty, of the familiar and the new, if they are to be reasonably satisfied with their environments.

Given the existence of memory, however it is obvious that the search for novelty is a never-ending job. A new event, once experienced, will not be new when we experience it again, for we recall its earlier occurrence. Several repetitions of the experience may be required before we can remember it clearly and conclude that it is no longer novel, but eventually we become "satiated" with the experience in this sense. It may continue to satisfy other needs, such as hunger, but even here we seem to prefer some variety in our diet. In general, though, it is the fact that man has a memory that forces him to keep moving; novelty, once understood and remembered, ceases to be novelty and thus ceases to satisfy the drive called effectance motivation.

The quest is actually made more difficult by the nature of memory. In the purely empirical sense, *every* experience is new, because no two events are ever precisely alike. The sense of novelty, however, comes not from the event itself but from our perception of it. Walter Lippman wrote, more than forty years ago, that man does not react to the world itself but to the picture of the world that he has in his head. In the same way, we identify an event by abstracting and symbolizing certain aspects of it.

These symbols constitute the substantive content of memory, and we evaluate an event according to the combination of symbols we have associated with it. If, after seeing a chicken for the first time, we abstract and remember only its size, shape, feathers, and sound, all chickens thereafter will seem the same and we will not feel a renewed sense of novelty when we see a new breed of chicken. Our "picture" of *chicken* will not be sufficiently elaborate for us to notice that there are interesting differences among various breeds of chickens.

Because one knows more about things that are important to him and because he employs a more complex set of symbols in identifying and remembering these things, it is reasonable to expect that he will find some fascination or novelty in the differences between two such things or events that one not familiar with them would find quite similar. He is better equipped to notice small differences that another person would miss, and to find them interesting. This situation might account for the familiar phenomenon of the "snowballing" of interest that a student experiences after he has acquired a certain amount of knowledge about a given topic. It can also explain why two chicken fanciers can discuss the fine points of chicken breeding with enthusiasm long after the topic has become quite boring to someone who knows little about chickens. White observes:

> Interest is not aroused and sustained when the stimulus field is so familiar that it gives rise at most to reflex acts or automatized habits. It is not sustained when actions produce no effects or changes in the stimulus field. Our conception must therefore be that effectance motivation is aroused by stimulus conditions which offer, as Hebb puts it, difference-in-sameness. This leads to variability and novelty of response, and interest is best sustained when the resulting action affects the stimulus so as to produce further difference-in-sameness. Interest wanes when action begins to have less effect; effectance motivation subsides when a situation has been explored to the point that it no longer presents new possibilities.[2]

The passage from White places more emphasis upon the individual's acting to produce novelty than we have, thus far.

This is an extremely important point—that the individual learns, quite early in life, that he can produce novel events in his environment through his own actions. He need not wait for the environment to produce novelty "by itself;" he is able to produce the same novel event repeatedly until he has grasped it and transformed it from the new into the familiar. The child psychologist, Piaget, cites example after example of small children doing this— seizing and letting go of toys, dropping a ball again and again, or biting things.

Not only does man have a memory which keeps changing his definition of novelty, but his memory requires organization. He needs order in his pictures of the world; he needs to understand in some way the relationships among the symbols and combinations of symbols that make up his memory. As man develops a more complex set of symbols, he requires less experience with a situation in order to remember it, but this simply frees him to undertake more exploratory activity. And, further, as man becomes aware of his ability to decide what parts of his environment he wishes to investigate, he usually develops criteria by which to make these choices. On this point White writes:

> We have to conceive further that the arousal of playful and exploratory interest means the appearance of organization involving both the cognitive and active aspects of behavior. Change in the stimulus field is not an end in itself, so to speak; it happens when one is passively moved about, and it may happen as a consequence of random movements without becoming focalized and instigating exploration. Similarly, action which has effects is not an end in itself, for if one unintentionally kicks away a branch while walking, or knocks something off a table, these effects by no means necessarily become involved in playful investigation . . . ; playful and exploratory behavior . . . is not random or casual. It involves focal *attention* to some object—the fixing on some aspect of the stimulus field so that it stays relatively constant—and it also involves the focalizing of *action* upon this object.[3]

Man, in other words, develops a sense of the relative importance of different kinds of novelty and will direct his exploratory efforts in some directions and not in others. He has begun to look for what we may call *meaningful novelty*. White suggests that the effectance motivation that underlies this type of interest is undifferentiated in infants and young children, but that later in life it may be the root of such varying motives as cognizance, construction, mastery, and achievement. I suggest here that it also forms the foundation of what we know as the urge to create. What is creativity, after all, if it is not the production of things or experiences that are meaningfully new?

The main link between effectance and creativity seems to lie in the process through which novelty is mastered, that is, the way in which novelty becomes understood so that it ceases to be novel. To "learn" something new, or, as White puts it, to extend one's ability to interact effectively with one's environment, requires more than simply the ability to identify a situation as having occurred before. It requires that one be able to relate this situation to other situations and to see its implications for future events. Rote learning, it is true, does not involve this, but it is not learning in the sense that we use it here. Learning requires relating new experiences to old.

The "old" experiences need not have been gained at first hand, either. As one acquires more knowledge both through personal experience and through increasing acquaintance with the body of mankind's accumulated knowledge, one's standards for judging newness become increasingly more stringent. Perhaps a major turning point in the process of socialization comes when the reported experiences of others tend to merge in the individual's mind with his own experiences, making it more difficult for him to find genuine novelty.[4]

It is in this way that effectance motivation in the individual is harnessed to society's standards of novelty so that the urge to create leads to products which others as well as oneself will define as meaningfully new, or creative. Not only the motivation to be creative but also a keen understanding of the current state of society's universe of discourse is required before one may hope to be recognizably creative. Ghiselin writes:

> Even the most energetic and original mind, in order to reorganize or extend human insight in any valuable way,

must have attained more than ordinary mastery of the field in which it is to act, a strong sense of what needs to be done, and skill in the appropriate means of expression. It seems certain that no significant expansion of insight can be produced otherwise, whether the activity is thought of as work or not. Often an untutored beauty appears in the drawings of children, and we rightly prize the best of them because they have wholeness of motive, but they have scarcely the power to open the future to us. For that, the artist must labor to the limit of human development and then take a step beyond. The same is true for every sort of creative worker.[5]

There are many people, of course, who as adults exhibit a less socialized form of effectance motivation. They are content to make birdhouses, collect buttons or stamps, build castles of matchsticks and glue, or to play the banjo. They may do very well in these activities, but without the desire to go beyond an existing, organized body of knowledge, they cannot be said to have a genuine desire to be creative.

Both the intensity of motive and the rigor of the standards by which one defines meaningful novelty probably vary from individual to individual, perhaps due partly to inheritance but probably in greater measure to upbringing. Creative people— those who successfully produce novelty that is meaningful and important to others as well as to themselves—seem to come from homes where "generalized curiosity" is encouraged, and we may assume that in intellectually or emotionally deprived homes such interests on the part of children are discouraged early in life. This is not the place to go intensively into what might be called the socialization of creativity, but I think the point has been established that creativity is a natural drive, which, in order to result in socially meaningful activity, must be shaped by society.

There remains the crucial question of why the creative person wishes to *share* his products with others. We may say that this tendency is "normal" in the creative person, if only because it is rare that people of this type seem to be more than mildly reluctant to exhibit their work when requested to do so. Carl Rogers remarks: "It is doubtful whether a human being can create without wishing to share his creation . . . He may put his discoveries in some cryptic code. He may conceal his poems in a locked drawer. . . . Yet he desires to communicate with a group that will understand him, even if he must imagine such a group."[6]

Creativity and Social Interaction

There is a very deep pleasure to be had in creativity, pleasure that seems at times to be related directly to the amount of struggle—even suffering—involved in the creative process. The roots of this pleasure, however, are difficult to establish. Presumably it is the pleasure of extending one's sense of order in the universe or of seeing that one has correctly grasped the idea of its order in a new way. At its peak, the pleasure of creativity is mystical rather than rational; it perhaps comes close to the *satori* experience of the Zen Buddhist, a sense of unity with the universe in which ordinary cognitive modes of perception are entirely transcended.

Because this type of pleasure is almost inaccessible to objective, scientific investigation, it is natural that we find more adequate treatment of it in fiction rather than in the reports of social sicentists' research. C. P. Snow, writing almost certainly from his own experience, describes the feeling in his novel, *The Search*:

> Then I was carried beyond pleasure. I have tried to show something of the high moments that science gave to me. . . . But this was different from any of them, different altogether, different in kind. It was further from myself. My own triumph and delight and success were there, but they seemed insignificant beside this tranquil ecstasy. It was as though I had looked for a truth outside myself, and finding it had become for a moment part of the truth I sought; as though all the world, the atoms and the stars, were wonderfully clear and close to me, and I to them, so that we were part of a lucidity more tremendous than any mystery. . . .
>
> Since then I have never quite regained it. But one

effect will stay with me as long as I live; once, when I was young, I used to sneer at the mystics who have described the experience of being at one with God and part of the unity of things. After that afternoon, I did not want to laugh again; for though I should have interpreted the experience differently, I thought I knew what they meant.[7]

Snow's phrase, "a truth outside myself," is particularly important here. After all, if creativity involves meaning, which in turn means that the created product is understandable in terms of some form of logic—whether it be aesthetic or scientific—, then it is only as the product embodies some sort of order that it can be appreciated even by its author. It might be said, in fact, that the creative person does not truly create, in the sense of making something out of nothing; instead, he discovers or expresses order that existed previously but beyond human awareness. We say that the scientist *discovers* a new law of nature, or that the artist *expresses* a feeling or view of nature. The specific arrangement of symbols on paper, or of material things, is of course empirically new, but its meaning, that by which we may grasp its newness, lies in its expression of some sort of order.

Barron may have had this in mind when he wrote:

One finds in creative writers a profound commitment to larger meanings of an aesthetic and philosophical sort which can find expression in the life work the individual has chosen for himself (or, as some have put it, in the life work that has chosen him).[8]

In much of what creative people have written about their own work, the impression is conveyed that they have felt possessed by the work, which seems to have an independent existence, and that the artist is only the vehicle through which the work gains objective existence. Thus Roger Sessions, a composer, writes:

The composer is not so much concious of his ideas as possessed by them. Very often he is unaware of his exact processes of thought till he is through with them; extremely often the completed work is incomprehensible to him immediately after it is finished.[9]

Just as the composer may feel that the work has come through, rather than from, him, so the performer may experience the same sensation.

> *Q*: How do you personally feel when you know that everything is going right while you are playing?
>
> *Janis*: Well, if all is going as it should, then I feel somewhat as if I'm detached from myself. I feel as if I am the instrument through which something is speaking. The feeling of humility is very great during moments like these. It's as if the music is coming through you. I sometimes think of it as "that divine feeling."
>
> *Q*: Would you say that this "something" is God?
>
> *Janis*: No . . . I can't say exactly what it is. It may be the creative spirit that animated the composer when he wrote the music. Or it may be the inner meaning of the music itself, which is essentially the same thing. I can only say that when a performance is going well, it's as if I am standing off from myself and watching while something else takes over.[10]

There is, then, often a strong feeling that one's created product has a goodness and an objective existence entirely independent of its creator, and sometimes even that it has a vitality of its own so that it has been able to use the individual in order to "make itself real." The ancient concept of being seized by the Muse also refers to this feeling. Much of the pleasure in creativity may come actually from the discovery of order within oneself; the creator experiences a *Eureka!* sensation upon bringing the product into existence and may feel that he has been more a spectator at the act of creation than the author who has been fully and consciously in command of the process.

It has often been remarked that artistic and scientific creativity for a man is the emotional equivalent of motherhood for a woman, and some have even suggested that it is for this reason that women are less likely to enter the creative professions: Their need for creativity can be satisfied biologically. Certainly there is some truth to the former assertion, if not necessarily to the latter, and it is interesting that "There is an apparent tendency to femininity in highly original men, and to masculinity in highly original women, but this may be a cultural interpretation of the generally increased sensitivity of the men and the intellectual capacity and interests of the women."[11] If nothing else, this suggests that creativity is an activity of human beings in general, rather than being related to sex, although it may be less likely to occur where the differences between the sexes are socially exaggerated.

Another point concerning creativity should be noted here, although it will be discussed in more detail in Chapter Five. This is the tendency for the creative person to be modest or ambivalent about accepting direct praise. I suggest that, at the psychological level, this is the individual's natural response to a situation in which he does not honestly feel that he can take full credit for what he has produced; if he were indeed a spectator at the act of creation, or were somehow given superhuman powers for a moment in order to produce his work, or he were not consciously in command of the creative process, it is natural that he would feel some hesitance about claiming full credit for his work. As we shall see later, this situation is compounded by the nature of the social system in which the scientist's work takes place.

At this point we have two possible explanations for the creative individual's immediate motivation to share his work. There is, first, his emotional reaction to what he has just produced; he has been present at the birth of something he believes to be wonderful, something that now has gained existence in its own right, and the creator may well need confirmation from others that his reaction to it is appropriate. Possibly the same sort of motive can explain the pleasure we find in telling jokes: We thought the joke was funny when we heard it, and wish to confirm this opinion by finding that others also find it funny.

Second, and perhaps more fundamental, is the simple need to find validation for one's cognitive evaluation of what one has created. We tend at first to doubt the very existence of something that is genuinely new, or at least to be dubious of our ability to evaluate it correctly, and we need at minimum the admission by others that this product *does* exist in its own right. Particularly when the product is extremely abstract and exists only as a few symbols on paper, its existence and meaningfulness may seem extremely implausible or fantastic to the author, and he may be more in need of others' response to it than the sculptor or engineer—whose products at least have three-dimensional existence. The need will of course vary also with the individual's level of self-assurance or "ego-strength," but even the strongest and most independent person seems occasionally to need reassurance from others that what he has created is valid and meaningful.

The need for cognitive confirmation of the existence and meaning of this product may, perhaps, be compared with the proselyting efforts of a religious convert. The convert has found a new and all-important truth, sacred rather than secular, and he must validate his impression that this truth is self-evident by asking others to perceive it also. He will have more difficulty than the scientist or the artist, however, because religious truth is assumed to be apparent to all men, whereas the accurate perception of scientific or artistic truth is usually thought to require a good deal of prior training. Members of some religious groups even conclude that the failure of non-believers to accept their views must result from purposeful misunderstanding, perhaps caused by the devil or else due to predestined damnation. The convert, in other words, looks for confirmation from everyone, whereas the scientist or artist is more frequently content with a more select audience.

The scientist may believe that another scientist who does not grasp the truth or importance of his work is merely lacking in sufficient intelligence or training. The artist, standing midway between these two types, tends more often to feel bafflement or anger at the "stupidity" of those who fail to appreciate his work. These responses to lack of appreciation, however, seem at base to reflect the same thing—that the creative person's "truth" has objective existence and meaning—and variation among these responses may be traced to various underlying assumptions about the type of truth in question.

I think, further, that we can perhaps find another answer to this question at a deeper level of meaning. This concerns man's sense of the *objective* existence of knowledge, his ability to conceive of knowledge as existing somehow apart from individual knowers and having a reality of its own. This idea leads naturally to the assumption that there is knowledge that is as yet unknown to us, an assumption underlying any "search for the truth." Such a conception of knowledge apparently develops whenever there arises a predominantly universalistic orientation among men, as in classic Greece and Rome and more generally in the Western World since the Renaissance, whenever a written language (particularly when it can be reproduced by printing) is available. It is expressed in such metaphors as Newton's famous description of himself: ". . . to myself I seem to have been only like a boy playing on the seashore, and diverting myself in now and then finding a smoother pebble or a prettier stone than ordinary, whilst the great ocean of truth lay all undiscovered before me."[12]

This faith in the independent reality of knowledge must be reinforced occasionally by empirical evidence, and I think this is to be found in the recording of knowledge. The distinction between what one man knows and what many men know is more than simply a matter of counting heads; something known to only one man is not knowledge "in the public domain" and cannot provide a basis for interaction. It is not what a man knows that influences his interaction with others, so much as it is his assumption that *they* know it also. The visible evidence that knowledge is shared—that one may count on others' knowing it—lies either in its being employed frequently in public discourse or else in its being recorded and made generally available to others. The latter is more important when the knowledge is complex and esoteric, and in this sense "the literature" of science is extremely important because it supports each scientist's assumption that his colleagues know or can know what he knows. And each feels a moral obligation to "keep up with the literature" so that this common faith in the sharedness of scientific knowledge is supported.

Given this need to support the independent existence of knowledge through providing evidence that there is concensus on its existence, it seems obvious that any new contribution to a body of knowledge must be recorded and made available to others. To tell a few people about one's discovery is not sufficient, for human memory is fallible. Knowledge may in an ideal sense be "out there," but only through its recording and thus preservation for general sharing can this faith be kept viable. Even a single typescript of a paper describing one's discovery is not sufficient, for it is not easily available to others and might disappear in a single accident.

Particularly because scholarly creativity is measured against this objective body of knowledge, the created product must be made apart of this same objective body of knowledge if it is to be meaningful. It must be made public, which means that it must be published so that it may be shared generally with others. Without the scientific community's awareness of its existence, the contribution does not have the same sort of objective existence than the body of knowledge to which it contributes has.

The creative person's desire to share his work, then, may be seen to have its roots in the very nature of creativity—the ability to produce novelty that is meaningful and important to others as well as to the creator. In terms of immediate motivation, he needs the affirmation of others that he has created something, that his contribution has objective existence, and in basic phenomenological terms, he is bound to share his creation if it is to be thought of as creative at all.

Certainly these arguments cannot be said to have been empirically demonstrated, for we have no knowledge of how many people there are who may create and then make no attempt to share their work. For the sociologist, however, such people are irrelevant, inasmuch as their creativity cannot, by definition, have any direct influence upon social interaction. At best, we may assume that the substantial majority of creative people feel a real need to share their creations and act upon this need.

Thus we may conclude that the need to share is an integral part of the creative experience; without the assurance that others are aware of one's work, the urge to create is not fully satisfied because creation has not yet really taken place, in the "objective" sense of the term. The creator of course hopes that others will indicate their awareness of his work in positive terms, but I believe that his essential need is for response of any kind—response that will confirm the independent existence of what he has created, even if it does not support his own evaluation of it.

Here we may see that the desire for response is not purely "utilitarian," as many have supposed. The creator does not wish to share his work simply for the sake of the practical advantages later to be gained if it is appreciated, although this possibility can certainly contribute to the desire to share the work. The need to share is, first of all, a need to complete the act of creativity. It is consummatory rather than instrumental; it is immediate rather than long-range; and it is rooted in the fact that creativity is inevitably a social as well as a psychological process.

Summary

This chapter has been devoted to demonstrating that the desire to create is entirely "natural" in man, that through socialization the desire is linked to shared standards of performance, and that the creator's interest in sharing his product is an intrinsic part of his desire to be creative. These assertions are, it is true, supported by logical analysis of the social implications of the key concepts used—creativity, novelty, meaning—and by reference to personal impressions and published descriptions of others' creative experiences, rather than by the use of experimental findings. I am not at all sure that these assertions *can* be directly tested through empirical research, for they are essentially interpretive rather than predictive.[13] Yet their implications can be tested at least for their "fit" with other theoretical structures. The next chapter will focus upon how these assumptions about the nature of creativity provide a foundation for viewing science as a social system.

Before proceeding to this task, it will be useful to indicate here certain important questions, implicit in this chapter, which will be treated in more detail in later chapters. Chief among these is the problem of the "appropriate audience"; it was suggested above that the creative person desires competent response from others rather than just any response, but the problem of identifying those who can give competent responses was not pursued. This is certainly a question concerning social structure and has important implications for defining the social boundaries of science and for analyzing the distinctions among the various creative professions.

Another question concerns the social practices through which the "current state of the art" is embodied and maintained so that it may serve as a collectively-accepted baseline against which future creative efforts may be assessed. Because the work of science is essentially cumulative, it is inevitable that this base-line is continually changing, and the means by which the scientific community is kept attuned to it will require considerable analysis.

Finally, there is the practical problem of how to distinguish between the unsung genius and the utter crackpot. Although the analysis of this matter will not provide a reliable means to solve the question, I believe that examining it in the context of what has been said here about creativity and what will be said in the next chapter about the social system of science, will enable us to see more clearly how geniuses actually *are* distinguished from crackpots in science today.

Footnotes for Chapter 4

1. For a somewhat different but highly useful treatment of this distinction, see H. Herbert Fox, "A Critique on Creativity in Science," in Myron A. Coler, ed., *Essays on Creativity in the Sciences* (New York: New York University Press, 1963), pp. 123–152.
2. Robert W. White, "Motivation Reconsidered: the Concept of Competence," *Psychological Review*, vol. 66 (1959), p. 322.
3. White, p. 322.
4. The need for the experience of novelty, however, seems sometimes to make us repress our knowledge of something we have experienced before. See Merton, "Resistance to the Systematic Study of Multiple Discoveries in Science," pp. 272–282.
5. Brewster Ghiselin (ed.), *The Creative Process* (New York: Mentor Books New American Library, 1955), p. 29.
6. Carl R. Rogers, "Toward a Theory of Creativity," in H. H. Anderson (ed.), *Creativity and Its Cultivation* (New York: Harper & Row, Publishers, 1959), p. 78.
7. C. P. Snow, *The Search* (New York: Signet Books New American Library, 1960), pp. 112–113.
8. Frank Barron, *Creativity and Psychological Health* (New York: Van Nostrand, 1963), pp. 242–243.
9. Roger Sessions, "The Composer and His Message," in Ghiselin, p. 49.
10. Harold Rogers, "Pianist Explains Power of Music Emotion: An Interview with Byron Janis," *Christian Science Monitor*, (December 9, 1964), p. 13.
11. Anne Roe, "The Psychology of the Scientist," in Paul C. Obler and Herman A. Estrin, eds., *The New Scientist* (New York: Anchor Book, Doubleday, 1962), p. 91.
12. Quoted in Robert K. Merton, "Priorities in Scientific Discovery: A Chapter in the Sociology of Science," quoted from Barber and Hirsch, p. 464.
13. For an excellent bibliography of work in the area of creativity, see Frank Barron, "The Psychology of Creativity," in *New Directions in Psychology II* (New York: Holt, Rinehart and Winston, 1965).

CHAPTER 5

The Social System of Science

I have defined a social system as a stable set of patterns of interaction, organized about the exchange of a qualitatively unique commodity and guided by a shared set of norms that facilitate the continuing circulation of that commodity. In Chapter Three a general model of social systems was presented; it focused on the fundamental importance in society of exchange and pointed out the three basic principles governing exchange relationships that are to be found in all social systems. These principles are, briefly, that one should want the commodity in question, one should obtain it through exchange with others, and that one should not employ behavior appropriate to obtaining one type of commodity in order to obtain a different type. Because there is a limited number of qualitatively distinct types of commodities that are of widespread and continuing interest to the members of society, we have only four major social systems in society: the economic, the political, the religious, and the family systems.

In the preceding chapter I suggested that the urge to be creative is widespread and continuing, and that the satisfaction of this urge requires exchange with others. In other words, there is a widespread and continuing interest in the commodity of "response to creativity," such that it may form the basis of a fifth social system within society. The terms of exchange in this social system are essentially the offer of one's creative work in return for response, competent evaluation, from others. The creative person, of course, hopes this response will be positive rather than negative, but I think that this hope is actually secondary to the basic need for response of any kind. The response to creativity is thus a commodity comparable to goods, power, love, and the affirmation of basic values; it may not be of as universal interest as are the other four, but so long as creativity is of continuing interest to a substantial number of individuals, it can form the basis of a social system in the same way that the other four do.

Having accepted for the moment the idea of a commodity, the acquisition of which is of continuing interest to scientists, our task is now to examine the norms and values that characterize the community of science. If these norms and values are to describe a social system, we assume they will embody the three principles that we have attributed to all social systems. It is to the norms of science that we next turn our attention.

The Norms of Science

We lack a clear-cut means for distinguishing between norms and values, but as a rule of thumb we can say that values concern primarily end-states or the characteristics of desirable goals, whereas norms pertain more to standards of behavior without direct regard for the purposes of that behavior. It is when behavior is judged with reference to its presumed goal, or when "proper behavior" itself is seen as an end rather than as a means, that the distinction between norms and values becomes blurred. Considering only the main distinction between them, we should speak of the *norms of science* rather than, as some have, the "values of science," for, as will become clear, norms concern mainly the sorts of behavior in which scientists should engage, rather than the goals they should seek.

The concept of "institutional values," the complex of norms and values that characterize a social system, enables us to think of the "rules" governing behavior in a given social system as though they were actually written down in law books or in its constitution. By thinking of them as being more explicit than they usually are and by examining the relationships among these rules, we can begin to get a clearer picture of the dynamics of the social system. In most cases they are *not* written out, and frequently we have taken them for granted since childhood. Thus it may be extraordinarily difficult to identify them objectively.

Because we tend to take these rules for granted, in our minds they shade and merge into one another so fluidly that any attempt to distinguish them—to say *this* is one norm and *that* is a different one—is bound to leave us with some feeling that we have done violence to reality by drawing these artificial distinctions. But without attempting to identify the various norms that govern a social system, we would make no progress at all in understanding it.

It is to the enduring credit of Robert K. Merton that he was able to conceptualize the norms of science, working presumably in part through intuition and testing his ideas against what scientists have said since the seventeenth century about their work and about how scientists should behave. Certainly a large part of work in the sociology of science today is based upon Merton's description of these norms, and the fact that his statement of them has continued to be used suggests that he cannot have been far wrong in identifying them as he did.

Yet no codification of such elusive materials can be accepted as final, and for different purposes it may be more useful to think of them in slightly different terms. If, then, the way that I identify the norms of science here differs somewhat from Merton's original definitions, it is in the interest of seeing whether an alternative strategy in analyzing the dynamics of science may not also be fruitful.

Merton identified four basic norms of science,[1] and Barber later added two more as being particularly relevant.[2] These six norms (or values) are the following:

UNIVERSALISM

This norm, orientational rather than directive in its intent, refers both to the assumption that physical laws are everywhere the same and to the principle that the truth and value of a scientific statement is independent of the characteristics of its author. In the words of Roger Coates, in his preface to the second edition of Newton's *Principia*, ". . . if gravity be the cause of the descent of a stone in Europe, who doubts that it is also the cause of the same descent in America?"[3]

It is this principle, too, which makes science an international community; what a Russian scientist discovers about the atom will be valid in America and his work can be appreciated by scientists everywhere. Empirical knowledge knows no national boundaries, and to reject his findings for political reasons would be totally irrational vis-à-vis scientific goals.

ORGANIZED SCEPTICISM

This norm is directive, embodying the principle that each scientist should be held individually responsible for making sure that previous research by others on which he bases his work is valid. He cannot be excused if he has accepted a false idea and then pleads innocence "because Dr. X told me it was true," even if privately we cannot accuse him of willfully substituting error for truth; he should have been properly sceptical of Dr. X's work in the first place. This is illustrated in Snow's *The Search* when the hero makes just such a mistake; as a result he is deprived of an appointment to head a new research institute, and an older scientist is commiserating with him:

> I had something like this on a smaller scale when I was younger than you . . . [;] you see, we both committed a crime against the truth. A crime in good faith, admittedly, honest, simply a mistake. . . . Now if false statements are to be allowed, if they are not to be discouraged by every means we have, science will lose its one virtue, truth. The only ethical principle which has made science possible is that the truth shall be told all the time. If we do not penalise false statements in error, we open up the way,

don't you see, for false statements by intention. And of course a false statement of fact, made deliberately, is the most serious crime a scientist can commit.[4]

The scientist is obligated also by this norm to make public his criticisms of the work of others when he believes it to be in error. It is not really difficult to agree with the statement that "a scientist is a man who has a quarrelsome interest in his neighbor's work."

It follows that no scientist's contribution to knowledge can be accepted without careful scrutiny, and that the scientist must doubt his own findings as well as those of others. He must hold himself entirely responsible for the goodness of his work.

COMMUNISM, OR COMMUNALITY

This norm directs the scientist to share his findings with other scientists freely and without favor, for knowledge that is not in the public domain cannot be part of the legitimate body of knowledge against which creativity is measured and to which other scientists refer in their work. Further, since other scientists cannot be expected to know what one is working on, this norm encourages the scientist to take the initiative in placing his findings before his fellow scientists.

DISINTERESTEDNESS

This orientational norm, in its broadest interpretation, makes it illicit for the scientist to profit personally in any way from his research. In Merton's original delineation of disinterestedness he relates it almost exclusively to prohibiting the scientist from making the search for professional recognition his explicit goal. (The importance of this point will be discussed later in this chapter.) Barber, however, pays closer attention to how this norm dissuades the scientist from an active interest in doing research as a means toward financial success or gaining prestige in the lay community. In general, it serves to encourage "science for science's sake" or to make research and discovery an end in itself.

Beyond these four norms, Barber has added two more: *rationality* and *emotional neutrality*. He also substitutes *individ-*

ualism for *organized scepticism* in his work, but this change involves only a minor shift of emphasis in definition.

Barber defines *rationality* essentially as a faith in the moral virtue of reason, pointing out that "the morality of science tends to drive it into *all* empirical areas. . . . This goal is based on the moral value that all things must be understood in as abstract and general a fashion as possible."[5] It may be interpreted also as the assumption that necessary to the achievement of the goals of science are (1) empirical test rather than tradition and (2) a critical approach to all empirical phenomena rather than acceptance of certain phenomena as exempt from scrutiny. Yet implicit here is the fundamental value placed upon *communicable* knowledge. "Rational," after all, refers not only to a kind of pragmatic perception of the relationship between ends and means but also to a standard for the assessment of persuasive argument. In the latter sense, the norm of rationality may more importantly refer to the necessity of maintaining a common set of standards by which proof may be demonstrated than to the inherently "expansionist" orientation of science. This point will be elaborated toward the end of the chapter.

Emotional neutrality, hand in hand with rationality and universalism, enjoin the scientist to avoid so much emotional involvement in his work that he cannot adopt a new approach or reject an old answer when his findings suggest that this is necessary, or that he unintentionally distorts his findings in order to support a particular hypothesis. It may well be that this norm is subsidiary to the four presented by Merton, for it is logically derivable from them, but it is important here to consider it alone in order to see its relations with the others.

Relations among the Norms

Given the assumption that logical, precise communication, generally denotative rather than connotative, is possible (the norm of rationalism as I have defined it here), and the assumption that the truth of empirical knowledge is independent of its discoverer and of time and place (universalism) the norms of science can, I think, be schematized as shown in the following table.[6] The two norms given under "knowledge" have not been discussed at length, but they seem to need little explication.

FOCUS OF NORM:	POINT OF REFERENCE:		
	The body of scientific knowledge	*Interaction among scientists*	*The scientist's psychological state*
Orientation	Objectivity	Organized scepticism	Emotional neutrality
Action	Generalization	Communality	Disinterestedness

Although these norms have been identified primarily in connection with science, it is obvious that they characterize in a more general way *all* fields of scholarly endeavor. They are appropriate to economic history as well as to physics, to philosophy as well as to geology, to English literature as well as to biochemistry. If "the truth" is the main objective of a group of people, norms such as those just described are necessary for it to continue its work and come closer to its goal.

But because "the truth" in different fields is subject to different standards of validation and significance, we find some differences in how these norms are interpreted in different fields. Science is concerned with empirical truth, whereas the fine arts focus upon aesthetic truth and theology upon spiritual truth. The means of demonstrating the truth and significance of a statement will thus vary. Ultimately, such demonstration in science requires the presentation of empirical evidence, whereas this is not usually possible in literary criticism or moral philosophy. When the consensus required for "certifying" a proposition as "true" cannot be arrived at through empirical operations, such as experimental verification in science, other means of achieving consensus must be employed. And when these means begin to involve rhetoric or personal influence, the norms of universalism and organized scepticism may be difficult to implement in practice.

This is not to say that these norms are not violated in science,[7] but simply that where there are intrinsic differences in the type of truth sought, there will be differences in how these norms are represented in patterns of behavior. This topic will be discussed again, from a different point of view, in a later section of this chapter.

Beyond demonstrating that these norms are to be found in many scientists' views of their work and in their sense of the rights and obligations that they should accept in their relations with other scientists, there has been some concern to identify the origins of these norms, or at least the reasons for their continued support by scientists. What, in other words, are the functions of this set of norms for science? Why is it that scientists feel so strongly that they must be upheld and enforced?

It is, of course, relatively easy to show that this combination of norms is admirably suited to ensure the optimal progress of science; ideally, only when scientists' behavior is guided by these norms is it possible to keep a continual check on the validity of new findings and to keep all scientists in touch with the frontiers of knowledge. Without the encouragement to share and to police each others' findings, and without the prohibition against orienting research to the acquisition of rewards extrinsic to science (for example, money, power, or prestige—all of which are ordinarily bestowed by non-scientists who cannot evaluate the goodness of scientific work), the doors would be open to secrecy, fraud, and log-rolling. Under such circumstances, the extension of knowledge would be seriously hampered if not stifled altogether.

Merton, although he recognizes the norms as "a distinctive pattern of institutional control of a wide range of motives which characterize the behavior of scientists," and warns against confusing "institutional and motivational levels of analysis," suggests no relationship between the two levels other than that of the functions of these norms for science.

A causal relationship between personal commitment to the norms and their relationship to the goals of science is obviously not intended. Yet Merton does not provide any other answer to the question of how these norms originated and of why scientists continue to view them as "right and good." To point out the functions of a set of norms—that is, their consequences for the continuing operation of the group as a whole—is not necessarily to explain how the norms originated and why they receive the support of the members of that group.

To be sure, it is possible for means to become ends, or for norms to be valued without regard to their relationship to goals, but this argument would have to imply that the occasional reinforcement necessary to maintain the patterns to which individuals are socialized must be based ultimately on the instrumental relation between these norms and the goals of science. One may, of course, assume that the group's members are aware of the relation between the norms and the group's goals so that they subscribe to the norms entirely for instrumental purposes. But this cannot explain how the norms come to have moral potency in their own right.

My basic argument here is that we cannot look to the functions of the norms of science in relation to the goal of science for an explanation of why scientists take them to be morally "right and good." The "functional-basis" argument seems inevitably to suggest a close correlation between personal commitment to "the advancement of knowledge in all science" (rather than "the advancement of knowledge of the topic on which I am working") and personal commitment to the norms of science. For myself, I find it difficult to accept this hypothesis.

An alternative explanation of the source of the moral force of the norms of science can be derived from our general analysis of the dynamics of social systems, namely, that the norms are important for the continued and just allocation of the commodity, in this case competent response, whose circulation forms the basis of the social system. Given people's general ability to reason from specific events to principles and to predict in a vague way the possible consequences of an act viewed as establishing a precedent, we can assume that when people are interested in continuing to obtain competent response to their creative work, they will be able to see what sorts of actions or patterns of action will be necessary.

I am suggesting that scientists subscribe to the norms of science first of all because of their importance for the continued, adequate circulation of the commodity in which they are mutually interested. This is not to say that all scientists are aware of this relation, but that through a combination of perceiving in a general way the necessity for such patterns of behavior, of training and mutual reinforcement, and of their congeniality with the personalities of many scientists, they have become institutionalized. It is the occasional reinforcement given these norms by the scientist's awareness of their relevance to his own interest in obtaining competent response to his work rather than to the general goal of science, which I feel accounts for their continuing moral potency. The norms are important to scientists because they concern something in which scientists have an immediate stake, not because they are beneficial over the long run to science as a whole.

It might be said, in fact, that some of these norms are natural concommitants of the desire to be creative. When the creator is uncertain of the meaningfulness of his product, his feeling is expressed in the norm of organized scepticism; when he wishes to share it with others, his desire is expressed in communality; and when he is truly modest about his work because it seemed to come *through* him rather than *from* him, he exhibits disinterestedness. To generate a norm from a personal feeling of course requires some modification of the immediate individual desire so that it can stand as a stable guide for interaction, both when the individual in question is responding to another's creativity and when he is seeking competent response to his own creativity. But it seems possible to conclude that the norms of science may be explained as well if not better through examining their relationship to the nature of creativity than through attributing their persistence and moral potency to their functions for the progress of science.

The arguments given above seem to answer one question that I think is not adequately handled in the Mertonian theory of science. This concerns the relationship between the norms of science and the reward-system of science. In the view presented here, the norms are derivative of scientists' interest in the reward, whereas Merton seems to be saying that the reward and the norms are separate consequences of a "deep devotion to the advancement of knowledge."

I do not think, however, that the explanation of the scientist's interest in professional recognition—the public assertion of favorable response—must be couched in either-or terms. It serves both functions, proclaiming successful role-performance as well as serving to complete the creative act. I am proposing here simply that the latter rather than the former is the fundamental basis of the scientist's interest in recognition.

There have always been, as Merton has pointed out, a certain number of men in science who see professional recognition as unrelated to either the goodness of their own work or the advancement of knowledge. Their image of themselves is so much determined by the attitudes of others toward them that they find recognition gratifying regardless of how it is gained. They may seek it simply to inflate their own egos or to use as a means toward some other end, but they value the *fact* of being recognized over the reasons for which recognition is given.

It is probably likely that there are more scientists who adhere to the norms of science than scientists involved in cases of scientific fraud, which gives testimony to the efficiency of the internal police system of science. But this fact is still not sufficient to support the idea that scientists adhere to the norms of science through fear of censure by their fellows, for it cannot explain the motives of other scientists who do the policing and who expose error when they find it. If men were punished as severely for sins of omission as they are for sins of commission, there would be no problem; but sins of omission are rarely dealt with so severely and we are left with the question of why men choose to expose error (or cheating) in science when it would be easier to ignore it. My answer is that they initiate criticism because this, too, is response to creative effort; criticism may itself be creative and thus needs the affirmation of others. Moreover, if a scientist were to give only positive responses to others' work, it would be either because some responses were dishonest or because some work was being deliberately neglected, violating the principle that *all* work should receive some response from other scientists.

In short, I am saying that scientists support the norms of science, through their own allegiance to them and through imposing sanctions on those who violate them, because they are in some sense aware that these norms are necessary if the exchange-system of science is to operate properly. Because each scientist, to the extent that he wishes personally to be creative, is interested in maintaining a social structure in which his efforts can continue to receive honest, competent response from others, he has a personal stake in supporting the norms that make this possible.

The Social System of Science

Let us now look more closely and systematically at the norms of science to see how they embody the three principles that, I have proposed, govern all social systems. This will require some slight departure from the description of the norms by Merton, but this change will be only one of emphases rather than of serious modification.

The first principle simply encourages one to participate in the social system, to seek the commodity that is exchanged within that system. *Communality* obviously serves this function through asking the scientist to place his work before his colleagues. In Merton's and in Barber's discussions of this norm, the emphasis is on its functions for the progress of science through making new knowledge available to all. Here, I would like to view the norm primarily as a specification of how one should participate in the system, that is, by offering one's work in return for competent response to it. It presupposes that the scientist has something to offer, or else encourages him to produce something that he can offer, and indeed makes this form of participation necessary for one to consider himself a scientist at all.

The second principle governing social systems concerns the source of the commodity one wishes to obtain. One should get it from others through exchange rather than create it for oneself or seize it. This principle is expressed in science in the norm of *organized scepticism*, although I think the norm should perhaps be generalized to the broader statement that one should respond to the contributions of others, both positively and negatively according to one's own evaluation of the contribution in question. The negative response is emphasized in most discussions of this norm for two reasons, that honest response is probably negative more often than it is positive and that the individual scientist must be sceptical of his own work and do his best to ensure its goodness before he places it before others.

A major focus of the norm, in other words, is the scientist's view of his own work. Not only should he look at others' work critically, so that he can give an honest evaluation of it, but he should not make the final decision as to how good his own work is. Thus, he should be interested in others' responses to his work, for without them, in principle anyway, he cannot come to an accurate evaluation of his own work. The norm acts as an injunction against the scientist's making his own final evaluation of his work, simultaneously protecting science against the crackpot (whose distinguishing characteristic is that he is insensitive to others' criticisms of his work—because he already "knows" how valuable it is) and supporting the exchange-system by insisting that the scientist look to his colleagues for final evaluation of his contributions.

The scientist may of course anticipate a favorable reaction from his peers; he may invest great amounts of emotion in his conviction that he is indeed correct in feeling that his work has been importantly creative, but he is prohibited from resting at this point. He must seek the reactions of others to his work, and must take account of them, for he is not allowed to claim that others' opinions are of no importance to him. It is usually the crackpot who makes this claim, and even if in fifty years he will turn out to have been correct, he is subject now to his colleagues' hostility because of his apparent arrogance and violation of this norm.

Not only, then, must the scientist seek the commodity in which the exchange system of science deals, but he is normatively prohibited from creating it for himself.

The third principle protects the autonomy of the social system by making it illicit for a participant to use "system-appropriate" behavior to acquire a commodity native to another social system. This principle obviously cannot be applied to actual human beings, for they must participate simultaneously (or sequentially) in most or all of the major social systems of a society. Its application must concern the attitudes and behavior appropriate to a social position, and thus to the individual only so long as he occupies this position.

It is probably this sort of injunction, which asks a man to compartmentalize the different roles he may play during the course of a day, that can most easily be violated with impunity, for although we may ask a man to change his behavior as he occupies different social positions, we are frequently unable to tell which position he considers himself to be occupying at a given time. Except for various clear-cut situations where the individual is required to adhere rigorously to one social position, he must make his own decisions as to which position he is occupying at a given time. (This, incidentally, may be one way a person is frequently able to rationalize and to justify behavior that seemingly violates his role obligations; he simply defines himself as occupying a different social position, one for which his behavior would be legitimate, and then justifies himself by pointing out the aspects of the situation that could be construed to legitimize him in this position.)

Yet each social system must have some norm that can be invoked to protect the integrity of its exchange system. In science, this function is most clearly served by the norm of *disinterestedness*. As was pointed out earlier, this norm acts primarily to prohibit the scientist from planning his work so that he will personally benefit from it in terms of money, influence, public esteem, or even professional reputation. Through making these other major commodities illicit as overt goals of the scientist's behavior *as a scientist*, this norm leaves him with only scientific criteria by which to determine what research to undertake. In particular, these criteria concern the importance of the work for the advancement of knowledge, or, more crudely, what he thinks other scientists will view as important and deserving of competent response.

Disinterestedness is related in two ways to the support of the exchange system of science. First, it helps to ensure that a scientist will work on problems of interest to his colleagues so that they will be more likely to pay attention to his work and to "reward" him with competent response. Second, it keeps him working on topics relevant to the work of others so that he will remain competent to respond to their contributions. To work on problems that are primarily of importance to nonscientists (the government, the industrial employer, the lay public) would make one run the risk of being separated from the central scientific universe of discourse. Further, and perhaps most immediately important, one who seeks an inappropriate commodity in return for his research efforts is in effect denying the importance to himself of the appropriate commodity and is thereby indicating not only his own lack of allegiance to science as a whole, but also, through setting a potential precedent for others, he is threatening the entire exchange system itself.

Here, then, we have the central structure of the social system of science, a simplified model that shows how the members of the scientific community can continue to engage in research, share their findings, and maintain a common universe of discourse. A viable social system must have members, a set of shared norms and values enabling the members to maintain stable interrelationships, and a distinctive incentive or reward, both psychologically meaningful and institutionally appropriate, motivating the members to continue their participation in this social system. As the preceding discussion demonstrates, science does have these characteristics: scientists are engaged in producing new empirical knowledge and want to obtain each others' evaluations of their contributions; the norms of science guide their behavior in these areas so that all scientists can participate in this type of exchange. The norms are so organized that they do not allow a "vicious-cycling" of the exchange process that would lead, sooner or later, to large numbers of scientists becoming discouraged and either quitting the system or else developing deviant practices.

The most important reasons, however, for saying that science may be viewed as a social system concern the relationship between the norms of science and the circulation of its native commodity or reward. The two factors are not independent of each other, as a functional explanation of the norms would imply. The preceding pages present a plausible, if not empirically verified, argument that the norms of science have their origins and their central importance in the maintenance of a social situation in which the commodity of honest, competent response to creative work can continue to be obtained by all members of this social system. The three elements that constitute the system are thus intrinsically interrelated, giving it greater stability and autonomy.

Perhaps because "competent response," unlike money and political stability, is valued for its own sake rather than as a means to other goals, science has the added advantage of recruiting mostly members who engage in research because they enjoy it. Its members do not undertake research because they must whether they like it or not (as the participants in the economic system must "earn a living" regardless of how much they enjoy it), which makes possible a greater degree of self-selection in recruitment to science and thus greater stability because nearly all scientists *want* to support the norms of science.

This analysis of the social system of science is not complete, however, without an examination of the other professions in which creativity is also a central goal. On the basis of the reasoning presented thus far, we should expect that the artist, the poet, and the engineer, as well as the scientist will endorse the norms of science. But we do not find these other professions spoken of as "communities," nor do we hear of references to their value-systems in the same way that these characteristics are attributed to science. They do not seem to exhibit the same degree of internal organization and coordination that characterizes science.

An attempt to explain these differences is necessary if we are to claim that we have described science accurately, for if we cannot explain why this description is not appropriate to the other creative professions, it would then seem that they should be organized just as science is—because they, too, are centered upon the act of creation—and that science is not distinguished by a social structure peculiar to itself.

Science and the Other Creative Professions[8]

Scientists, engineers, writers, and artists are usually thought of as being quite different types of people. Certainly the types of social organization that have developed in connection with each of these enterprises differ considerably from each other. Yet the creative act, the *summum bonum* of each profession, seems to be at base the same, whether it results in a scientific discovery, a new design for a valve, a poem, or a painting. We assume that any type of creativity needs response, and thus we might reason that all of the creative professions should approximate the social system of science as it has been described here. But they do not, and I think it is possible to explain why by reference to two social-structural variables that pertain to all of these professions.

These variables are: first, the nature of the creative product (is it verbal or is it concrete?), and second, the nature of the normatively appropriate audience for this product (is it composed of "experts" or of the general public?). The former variable is important in that it determines whether or not the created product can be easily reproduced and distributed: a verbal product is capable of almost infinite duplication and can be distributed through the mail at reasonable cost, whereas a concrete product (a painting, a piece of sculpture, or a radar component) is much more costly to reproduce and it may also be costly to distribute these copies.

The latter variable—the kind of audience—determines whether or not the creative individual can expect to engage in the reciprocal exchange of "competent response" with his audience; if only other creative people in the same field make up the audience, then all may seek and give this commodity, whereas when the audience includes a large proportion of laymen, the creative person must resign himself to response the technical competence of which he cannot assess, and must also accept the fact that because most of the members of his audience are not themselves creative in his field, they will not be interested in obtaining his evaluation of their work and therefore will not necessarily be interested in maintaining regular relationships of reciprocal response to the products of each other's work.

The importance of this second variable and its relevance to all fields of creativity may be seen in the distinction between what might be called "basic" and "applied" work in each area. In engineering there are "blue-sky" engineers as well as draftsmen; in literature we find *belles-lettres* distinguished from hack-work; and in the arts there is "established," "serious," or *avant-garde* work as opposed to "popular" work. In music, too, artists who have "gone popular" or "gone commercial" are hotly criticized in some quarters. The question is whether the individual is contributing to the advancement of his field or whether he is simply drawing on what others have done in order to make money or to satisfy an unsophisticated audience. The temptation to follow this second path is a prominent theme in much fiction about creative people, the basic plot showing the difficulties involved in remaining "pure" when there is so little public support for it.[9]

The following chart orders the four major fields of creativity according to these two variables, and adds some more specialized areas that seem to crosscut these fields.

The basic argument here is that a social system, identifiable by the fact that its members have special rights and duties toward one another, can develop in a creative field only when the legitimate audience is limited to "experts," (generally, others who are also creative in that field) and when the product can be easily distributed throughout this audience. Under these conditions, each participant can both give and obtain the commodity of competent response and can do this with relative ease. In other words, the allocation of the incentive that motivates its members is controlled collectively by the group, and the rules governing its allocation are effective because all members are interested in it.

For these reasons science has been the only one of the creative professions to develop an identifiable social system. Contributing further to the integration of this system is its focus upon the generalization of knowledge, which means that the work of one scientist may have implications for the work of many others even though they may be working on different specific topics. Audience-interest is thus wider in basic science than, say, in engineering, which increases the probability that a scientist will receive response from a variety of other scientists.

THE CREATIVE PROFESSIONS, ORDERED BY
NATURE OF PRODUCT AND NATURE OF AUDIENCE

NATURE OF THE PRODUCT CREATED

Verbal   *Concrete*

Architecture

Information theory, computer technology

ENGINEERING

THE ARTS

SCIENCE

LITERATURE

Dance, music, and drama

Humanities
Social Sciences

NORMATIVELY APPROPRIATE
AUDIENCE

"Experts"

General Public

Engineering (which I have distinguished from "applied science" on the basis of its direct and primary concern with the building of concrete, working physical systems) is handicapped by just that fact, its products are concrete and thus not capable in themselves of having logical implications for the work of many other engineers. One engineer's work, material objects produced to serve a practical need by a specified time, cannot be of immediate importance to engineers in other fields in the same way that one scientist's work may affect the work of his colleagues. Nor can the engineer as easily make his work known to a wide audience of engineers; he cannot "publish" it. A published blueprint would not in itself be sufficient information to provide a basis for obtaining a competent response; the importance of "working out the bugs" in an engineering product seems to illustrate the fact that a blueprint, including verbal and mathematical details, is not necessarily adequate as a substitute for the concrete product.

This means that it is not ordinarily possible in engineering to obtain response from the profession as a whole as readily as one may in science; at best, the feedback would be too slow to make it a compelling incentive. And without such a worthwhile incentive, native to a given area of endeavor and negotiable in reciprocal exchanges, an autonomous social system cannot develop.

In the case of literature and the arts, the major difficulty is that the legitimate audience consists mainly of people not themselves working in these fields. Regardless of the means through which agreement on what constitutes "truth" in a field is achieved, when only a few members of the audience can be expected to contribute to the field themselves, no symmetrical exchange-relationships can be established. The commodity of competent response cannot *circulate*, inasmuch as the members of the audience are not interested in the writers' or artists' response to *their* creative efforts, that is, there is no opportunity for the artist to play the role of audience, and so a genuine social system cannot come into existence.

To be sure, there are elites who are presumed to have special competence in judging literary and artistic work, but they do not have the same clear-cut identity as a competent audience that scientists and engineers have for each other, nor are they always composed of people who are themselves creative in these areas. Although the creator is thus particularly interested in these people's evaluation of his work, he and they cannot engage in the reciprocal exchange of competent response. Perhaps the Russian practice of letting the musician or the actor applaud his audience while he is being applauded, or the more widespread practice of the creative performer's thanking his audience for being "a good audience," suggest that a desire for reciprocity is present even in the absence of an appropriate commodity.

The various fields of creativity that I have indicated as straddling the line between the two types of audiences seem to be particularly subject to conflicting standards of excellence, insofar as the professionals and the lay public differ in what they will accept as good work. Because work in the humanities and social sciences has implications for everyone, particularly as it may impinge upon social values, the public does have some interest in their products and may occasionally insist that its standards of acceptability be adhered to. Legal battles over the banning of certain books as obscene, or over the ethics of social research, are a case in point. And it is of course difficult for men working in these fields to claim that the public has no right to an interest in their work. Architects, too, must usually compromise between what the public will support and what, ideally, they would like to create.

In the fields which straddle the verbal-concrete distinction between types of creative products, the major problem is not one of standards but of assembling the facilities necessary for presenting these products. To the extent that a creative product exists not as a concrete object (for example, a book, a transistor, a building, or a picture) but as a pattern of activities through time (for example, the performing arts), there may be considerable difficulty in presenting it to a large audience. The more financial cost preparing its presentation entails, the more it will have to be "pitched" to the level of appreciation of a large audience, which generally means restricting the creative element in it a good deal. There may be also difficulty in ensuring the same quality of performance time after time. To the extent that such performances can be "reproduced" and made widely available (as, for example, through the commercial recording of music on records and tape and the recording of dance and drama on film and video tape), these fields tend to resemble the cell in which we have placed literature in the chart.

When an organized "presentation," combining different arts and artists is called for, it means also that the audience will evaluate performances and performers as well as the creator himself, so that credit for creative work in drama, music, and the dance, must be divided among several individuals. It is often difficult for them to decide privately who among them should receive more credit for the success (or failure) of the performance. Did the actor save the play, or the play save the actor? There is an inherent vagueness in feedback here that may prevent the creative person from feeling that he has obtained an accurate evaluation of his own contribution to the performance, which in turn works to prevent the development of a stable social system in any of these fields of creativity.

In seeking the determinants of the kinds of social organization that are found in the various areas of creativity besides science, the fundamental point to be made is that when the commodity of competent response cannot be used to help establish an autonomous social system, commodities native to the rest of society must be used to organize the relations among people in these areas. This usually means involvement with the economic system. In engineering, the "significant other" is the employer; in literature it is the publisher; and in art it is the gallery owner or buyer of a work of art; in theatre, the producer or a ticket-buyer.

For the engineer, a promotion or a raise in salary must serve as the major indication that his work is appreciated, whereas a "sale" serves the same purpose for the writer and the artist. The fact, however, that promotions may be made by technically incompetent people, and that someone with little taste can purchase a book, record, or painting, means that such indications of appreciation cannot be trusted. Creative people therefore tend to be ambivalent about the matter, hoping that a promotion or a sale is a sign of creative success but realizing that this may not be so. Too much financial success for an artist, as a matter of fact, may be taken by his peers as a sign that he has *not* been artistically successful; a product that appeals to a very large number of people must, they assume, obviously involve a relatively low degree of genuine creativity, else it would not command such a wide audience.

To conclude: we do not find a set of special norms governing the relationships among engineers, writers, or artists, as we do in science. The sociologically significant aspects of their creative products are such that the development of an autonomous social system of engineering, or literature, or art is simply not possible. We may find the beginnings of a social system only when such people, for example artists, are gathered together and can engage in face-to-face relationships. Artists' and writers' colonies and summer conferences are perhaps so popular because they provide a situation in which there is a technically competent audience to provide appreciation for good work and where the coin of appreciation is reciprocally valuable. Good engineering laboratories appear to embody a similar situation. But only in science, because of the special characteristics of its creative product, has there developed a true social system.

At base, then, whereas creativity may be essentially the same in all fields, the nature of its product and its audience seems to determine the kind of social organization that will be associated with it. And because the type of social organization in which a creative person is involved is so important in directing his everyday behavior, it is no wonder that as we look at the artist and the engineer, the poet and the scientist, we may have difficulty in recognizing the same creative process in all.

Summary

In this chapter I have described the basic structural characteristics of science in social-system terms, pointing out that its own "native commodity" circulates among scientists in accordance with a set of norms that embody the three principles discussed in Chapter Three, that govern social systems. The central idea, of course, is that when all parties concerned both want and can bestow the commodity in question, in this case competent response, they will develop a set of norms governing their relationships that will facilitate the continuing, satisfactory circulation of this commodity, and thus establish what I have termed a social system.

The ideas developed here have drawn heavily upon the work of Robert K. Merton, departing from his analysis of science only in the minor redefinition of the norms of science and extending his concept of professional recognition to the more general one of "competent response" as the actual reward-medium. This has then led to a reformulation of the central functions of the norms of science and to a rather different view of the motivational basis of their continued support by scientists. Whether or not this analysis serves to advance the sociology of science, Merton's work still stands as the foundation of this analysis and of nearly all other current work in the field.

Because this analysis is based largely on a concept of social systems and because data are not at hand that can directly test its validity, demonstration of the model's utility must rest mainly upon its provision of logically satisfying explanations of certain important aspects of science. Thus, this chapter has concluded with a discussion of how science can be sociologically distinguished from the other creative professions; the next chapter focuses more closely on several key aspects of the social structure of science in an attempt to demonstrate further the utility of the model.

Footnotes for Chapter 5

1. "Science and Democratic Social Structure," pp. 550–561.
2. Bernard Barber, *Science and the Social Order* (New York: Collier Books, Crowell Collier and Macmillan, Inc., 1962), pp. 122–142.
3. Roger Coates, "Preface," in the Motte translation of Isaac Newton, *Principia*, 1713.
4. C. P. Snow, *The Search*, p. 281.
5. Barber, *Science and the Social Order*, p. 87.
6. This table is the product of several discussions on the basic values of the academic profession with Talcott Parsons, Gerald M. Platt, and others.
7. See, for instance, Alfred de Grazia, ed., *The American Behavioral Scientist*, vol. 7, no. 1 (September 1963), an issue entirely devoted to "The Politics of Science and Dr. Velikovsky."
8. This section is based on N. W. Storer, "Science and the Creative Professions," presented at the annual meeting of the Eastern Sociological Society, April 7–8, 1962, in Philadelphia.
9. For example, Dorothy Baker's *Young Man With a Horn*, Sinclair Lewis' *Arrowsmith*, Norbert Weiner's *The Tempter*, and Mitchell Wilson's *Live With Lightning*.

CHAPTER **6**

Critical Aspects of the Social Structure of Science

In this chapter we shall turn our attention from the "ideal" organization of science, the social *system* of science, to a consideration of certain general patterns of behavior in which scientists actually engage. Such patterns constitute the social *structure* of science. The principal distinction between system and structure, as I use the terms here, lies in the fact that *structure* represents the working out of *system* in the "real" world. It is influenced not only by what men want to do or think they ought to do but also by what they are realistically capable of doing. A social structure may thus be seen as a relatively stable set of behavior patterns that emerge as a compromise between normative ideals (the "cultural structure," in Merton's terms[1]) and the constraints imposed upon men's activities by such factors as space, time, energy, incomplete information, and the characteristics of other individuals as physical organisms.

The attempt to explain certain aspects of the social structure of science in terms of the model developed in the preceding chapters obviously will not prove that the model is "true" or "false"; rather, my hope is to demonstrate its general adequacy in helping us understand the scientific community. The following discussion will be based on the assumption that whereas the norms of science are indeed functional with respect to its purposes as a collectivity—the extension of certified knowledge—they are not of teleological origin, coming *sui generis* from outside the minds of scientists. They are, instead, founded in scientists' desires to obtain competent response to their work. From this point of view, Merton's conception (1963b, p. 270) of the scientist's "deep devotion to the advancement of knowledge as an ultimate value" expresses the logical extension of the scientist's desire to be creative. He wishes to be creative within a universalistic framework, vis-à-vis an objective body of knowledge, and his commitment to the advancement of knowledge is a generalization of his personal interest in the very terms by which creativity is defined.

To be sure, the scientist's definition of what constitutes acceptable creativity is usually given precision through his training in science. Through this he learns the specific patterns of behavior that embody the norms of science and develops his conception of his "audience." The training process links a basic motive to a social structure, rather than creating a new motivation; his acceptance of this structure and of these norms is based on his awareness that they make it possible for him to do what he wanted to do originally—to be creative.

My concern in this chapter, then, is to show that the conception of science as a social system will give us real assistance in explaining certain of the more puzzling social practices among scientists and in understanding the major "social problems" that seem to beset science as a whole.

I have suggested that the stability of the social organization of science is maintained because its major norms embody the three basic principles governing all social systems. It follows that most of the "problems" of science as a whole develop out of the violation or potential violation of one or more of these norms and that many of the activities of scientists, which may seem difficult to explain, are in fact attempts to avoid such violations or to cope with their inevitability. Thus, both the social problems of science and the accepted practices of scientists are rooted in the norms of the social system. In particular, these are the norms of disinterestedness, organized scepticism, and communality, and I shall use these concepts to order the following discussion.

Scientists are motivated to identify such problems, and to develop patterns of behavior that circumvent them because of their interest in maintaining a social structure through which they can continue to carry out their activities with reasonable satisfaction. In the analysis to follow, I will try to show that it is this concern, the wish to be able to continue to receive competent response to one's creative efforts, rather than commitment to the general advancement of knowledge that underlies the basic patterns of behavior composing the social structure of science.

Of the three norms I have identified as being of fundamental importance to the social system of science, disinterestedness is the only negative one. That is, it is the only one specifying what one should *not* do. It negatively identifies one of the more serious social problems of science if only because sins of commission are more visible than are sins of omission. The sometimes agonized ambivalence that scientists exhibit toward professional recognition seems to have its roots in this norm, as does the invidious distinction often made between basic and applied research.

The norm of organized scepticism is involved when the problem of distinguishing between the unsung genius and the crackpot arises as well as in other, lesser problems. Finally, the norm of communality is particularly relevant whenever questions arise concerning access to channels of communication within science, as well as when security regulations clamp down on the scientist's freedom of communication.

Problems of this kind, it should be noted, are rooted wholly in the social structure of science; they would occur even if science existed in a vacuum. But science exists in a larger social environment whose changes, either slow or rapid, create additional problems for science. These tend to be problems with which the norms of science are not prepared to deal; they concern what might be called in the broadest sense "inflation" and "deflation." By these terms I mean changes in the supply of the commodity around whose circulation the social system is organized, relative to the demand for it. We may say initially that the norms of any social system are predicated on the assumption of a given "level of scarcity" of the commodity—"scarcity" here being a function of both the absolute supply of the commodity and the number of individuals currently trying to obtain it—and that the norms consequently are not prepared to deal with problems that occur as a result of changes in these parameters of the situation.

As has been the case historically with both the economic and the political systems, change in either the amount of the commodity available or in the number of persons seeking it, or in both simultaneously, will have extremely important consequences for the structure of the system. The social structure of science is today experiencing such changes in terms of the "publication explosion" and its own "population explosion." The next chapter, on the future of science as a social system, will be concerned with the problems engendered by these changes and how science is responding to them.

Problems Involving
Disinterestedness

This norm, it will be recalled, is focused essentially upon preserving the integrity and the value of science's "native" commodity by discouraging the scientist's interest in other commodities as incentive for his work. Each social system within society must be reasonably successful in maintaining the value of its own commodity for its participants and in maintaining a distinction between the behavior patterns through which it is obtained and those through which other commodities are obtained. If it is unable to do this, it will lose its identity and through dedifferentiation will merge with one or more of the other social systems. The difficulty in keeping one commodity separate from another seems to vary, to a large extent, with the probability that the two will be involved in the same concrete situations. For instance, because the control of material goods and the control of others' actions are closely related, either commodity facilitating acquisition of the other, historically it has been particularly difficult to differentiate the economic and the political systems.

The difficulty is even greater when something that ordinarily represents the concrete embodiment of one commodity may be viewed also as the embodiment of another. Money given as a gift or a prize may be viewed either as an expression of affection or honor or simply as the commodity native to the economic system. How it is viewed by the recipient will have consequences for his response to it, so there is some concern on the part of each party involved to know how the other will define the situation. Here, the distinction between social systems, between patterns of interaction focused upon the exchange of different commodities, must be maintained through normative control of the individual's definition of the situation rather than by the physical separation of commodities or activities. Maintaining these distinctions is extremely important in science.

AMBIVALENCE TOWARD PROFESSIONAL RECOGNITION

In science, the commodity of professional recognition, the concrete embodiment of competent response to creativity, may be viewed not only as competent response but also as the foundation of influence. Ideally, in terms of our analysis of creativity, the scientist should view competent response as an entirely consummatory commodity, necessary to complete the act of creation but otherwise completely unimportant. However, because such response is typically recorded, made public in some form, it inevitably has relevance to the scientist's relationships with his colleagues. Every social structure requires that participants be able to trust one another, and this trust is usually founded on past performance. In science, a man's past performance is indicated by his "store" of professional recognition, which thus helps his colleagues gauge the amount of trust they may invest in him and in what areas.

Despite the strongly egalitarian ethos of science (scientists should treat each other as equals, both because a man's personal characteristics are assumed to be unrelated to the quality of his contributions to knowledge and because inequalities among them might interfere with free and open communication), scientists do acquire reputations on the basis of past work and tend to be ranked in a hierarchy of excellence. The higher a scientist is in this hierarchy, the more likely his colleagues are to trust him to do good work and to pay serious attention to his response to their work. The receipt of professional recognition thus confers some amount of authority upon a scientist; achievement is *ascribed* to him, with the result that he may be able to influence the work and opinions of other scientists simply on "authority," because he is a "great man," rather than on the basis of rational scientific persuasion.

Authority of this sort is ordinarily thought to be gratifying and worth seeking. But to seek it would be to substitute a different commodity, the ability to influence others because of what one has accomplished in the past rather than through the acceptable mechanisms of rational argument and empirical demonstration, for that of competent response. Yet the two aspects of professional recognition cannot be separated, so the norm of disinterestedness must operate to make scientists ignore the authority-conferring potential of recognition. It involves them in an implicit conspiracy to deny this potential and may thus account in part for the ambivalence they demonstrate when faced with the problem of admitting how much they really desire professional recognition.

From this point of view it might be said that scientists support the norm of disinterestedness, in this instance showing ambivalence toward professional recognition, because they have perceived the importance to the maintenance of the social system of keeping separate the two commodities represented in professional recognition. Yet I believe we can trace the basic motivation to support it back to the scientist's personal interest in obtaining competent response to his work and need not depend upon his sociological awareness of the function it has. The following discussion will demonstrate that this is one of those "happy circumstances in which moral obligation and self-interest coincide and fuse."[2]

The more authority a scientist has, the more difficulty he may experience in obtaining genuinely honest evaluation of his contributions. His colleagues may feel it unnecessary to examine his work carefully, assuming that he can be trusted to avoid errors. If they are his juniors, they may be unwilling to voice criticisms of his work because he is a "great man" and criticism would only expose their own inadequacies or because his opinion of their work is so important to their own careers that they are afraid of offending him. And whereas critical response may be weakened, so, too, on the same grounds may expressions of approval from his colleagues come to be suspect; they may be merely flattery rather than competent evaluation.

Not only may the establishment of a reputation or of authority on the basis of professional recognition reduce the validity of response to one's future work, but this validity may be more directly undermined. Given the dual nature of professional recognition, by the very act of admitting a personal interest in recognition, the scientist threatens the value of the commodity he seeks. Because praise from one's colleagues is not intrinsically related to the goodness of one's work, the scientist's trust in the impersonal objectivity of their response to his creativity is weakened as soon as he has indicated that he seeks praise rather than evaluation. He has opened the way for his colleagues to use the bestowal of professional recognition for their own ends. Further, the admission of such an interest may appear to be a request that one's colleagues violate their own standards of objectivity, so that for this reason as well the scientist will be reluctant to voice his interest.

Here, then, the scientist's ambivalence toward professional recognition is not only an expression of disinterestedness—his wish to avoid making the authority accompanying recognition a legitimate goal within science—but also a necessary consequence of his interest in supporting the value of the commodity as genuinely trustworthy response to creativity. Merton's explanation of scientists' ambivalence toward professional recognition is based upon their having internalized two potentially conflicting values: ". . . the value set upon originality, which leads scientists to want their priority to be recognized, and the value set upon humility, which leads them to insist on how little they have in fact been able to accomplish."[3] Certainly the conflict between these values must play a part in producing ambivalence, but I think an explanation that relates this ambivalence more directly to the scientist's own needs and activities, as well as to the functional needs of science, offers a more complete picture.

If indeed the real value of professional recognition to the scientist lies in its function of completing the creative act, this value may be expected to depreciate quite rapidly. Its character as a reward is fulfilled with its receipt rather than in its later "use" in an instrumental fashion, so that last year's recognition will no longer be rewarding to the scientist today. It may be partly for this reason that we find world-renowned scientists as highly motivated in their research activities as are their junior colleagues and for this reason also that distinguished scientists at the end of their careers often display such modesty about their achievements. The previous recognition they have received has become stale to them; what was once new and creative has become scientific commonplace, so that in retrospect their careers seem dull and flat. Merton cites Lagrange's summary of his lifetime of discovery as "I do not know," and the reported deathbed statement of Laplace: "What we know is not much; what we do not know is immense."[4] There is no way to prove that such statements are not the result of the norm of humility internalized, but the alternative view—that these statements are a natural consequence of the transitory value of professional recognition—seems an equally adequate explanation.

I have thus far been concerned with scientists' ambivalence toward professional recognition as a case in which the norm of disinterestedness operates to make scientists deny the value to them of influence and authority in science. That their motives in denying this interest stem from their desire to maintain the value of recognition as competent response does not mean that their behavior does not fulfill also the function of protecting the autonomy of the social system of science. Another commodity, perhaps more obviously in competition with competent response as a legitimate goal of the scientist, is money. In the following section I will discuss the distinction between basic and applied research, and the invidious comparison often made between them, as being explainable also in terms of the norm of disinterestedness.

THE INVIDIOUS DISTINCTION
BETWEEN BASIC AND APPLIED SCIENCE[5]

The distinction between basic and applied research has long been a source of difficulty for those trying to speak intelligently about different types of research. The dilemma has been defined by Kidd in this way: If we wish to make the distinction on the basis of the eventual consequences of the research findings, then we must either wait a long time after the research has been carried out before deciding into which category it falls or else engage in some fairly risky prophecy about its consequences. If, on the other hand, we wish to base the distinction upon the researcher's motivations, we run the risk of including a lot of inconsequential research (busy-work, poorly conceptualized work, research that did not pay off in application) in the category of basic research (See Kidd, 1959, p. 369). From our point of view, we are naturally more interested in the latter sort of definition, for we are interested in the scientist's motivation rather than in the consequences, if any, of his work. Of even more interest to us is the social distinction often made between the two types of research; it should be clear to anyone who has had extensive contact with scientists that the distinction has definite meaning for them and that it often carries invidious connotations as well. The distinction is usually felt to be a matter of private opinion and inappropriate for discussion in print, but the existence of occasional ill feeling between scientists who define themselves as "basic" and those whose interests are primarily "applied" cannot be denied.

Although it would be difficult to provide extensive documentation of this usually covert rivalry, there are some references here and there to the existence of the rivalry. Barber, for instance, reports that " 'Pure' scientists are said to have 'better' motives than 'applied' scientists," although, further, he indicates that "there is no firm way of determining the correctness of such allegations."[6] Other, more direct criticisms of basic science also appear from time to time: ". . . too basic for the hardbitten practical man, . . . too applied for the purists,"[7] and ". . . I can easily go on adding illustrations from this sort of 'horribly applied' work, as one of our friends once facetiously called it."[8]

Hagstrom quotes another example of the "inferior" place held by applied research, in discussing informal pressures that may come to bear upon scientists to select some research problems rather than others:

> An applied mathematician spoke of the difficulty of getting other applied mathematicians appointed in his department: "We want an applied mathematician. I'll suggest a man, but I must be careful to suggest one the pure mathematicans consider to be a mathematician. For

example, . . . one man in our department turns out much good mathematics—good from an engineer's standpoint; but he is ostracized by the pure mathematicians, considered inferior by them. . . . It's hard to say. Mathematitions don't feel any creativity is involved in his work. He applied standard techniques to new problems. He may be ingenious, but it is not mathematical creativity."[9]

The following remarks express, in exaggerated form, the arguments one might hear from a member of each camp: The basic scientist feels that applied scientists are not creative, that applied work attracts only mediocre men, and that applied research is like working from a cookbook. For his part, the applied scientist might well counter with the imprecation: The basic scientist is a snob, working in his ivory tower and afraid to put his findings to a real test; he is like Bacon's spider, spinning webs out of his own substance while we in applied research are making real progress.

Parenthetically, I should note that the question of whether a given scientist is "basic" or "applied" is not really at issue; it is his colleagues' definition of his attitude that is crucial, and the crude index of his allegiance to science is most often his place of employment. It is true that there are many scientists in industry who are more concerned with the scientific community's opinion of their work than with what their employers think, and there are certainly some scientists in universities who are more interested in public acclaim than in professional recognition; in matters of this sort, however, scientists, like other men, tend to deal in generalities.

The expressions of such attitudes toward "basic" *vs.* "applied" researchers may be said to be oriented toward myths or ideal types rather than toward specific individuals. The two sorts of researchers, if indeed scientists may be so neatly divided into two groups, remain one in the eyes of the public; they receive their training in common, may well read the same journals, and cannot afford to "break off diplomatic relations" with each other. In the face of such sentiments, certain conventional sympathies have arisen to ease the conflict. The basic scientist may be pitied for his inbility to escape the sterile ivory tower, whereas the applied scientist also is pitied because of his anxiety that others will not appreciate the scientific value and importance of his work and because he is "controlled" by non-scientists. The man who leaves the university for work in industry may be supposed to have heavy debts that account for his leaving the "natural home" of basic research, and the man who moves from industry to academia might be described as being unable to keep up with the pressure to produce practical results.

Another means of reducing the potential hostility between the two types is to deny that the distinction exists at all, usually through ignoring the social context of research altogether. "Scientific research is only good or bad, not basic or applied. Good science consists of original thinking about careful observations in interesting situations, and frequently a practical question is the stimulus for it. The false dichotomy of 'basic' and 'applied' too often reinforces a precociousness or snobbery in the graduate student that narrows his vision for years after leaving the academy."[10]

However, none of these opinions, neither those expressing the potential conflict nor those attempting to minimize or ignore it, are sufficient to explain the distinction and its importance in the social structure of science. Barber (1952, pp. 98–102) has discussed in detail the empirical differences between basic and applied research, and these differences undoubtedly bring about a self-selection of different types of scientists for one type of research or the other. The picture is further confused by the operation of a self-fulfilling prophecy that seems to result in, among other things, the discouraging of more talented graduate students from entering applied work (Marcson, 1960b, p. 54).

Our assumption is that whatever antagonisms exist between basic and applied researchers, they cannot be attributed to differences in intelligence, skills, or achievements. They seem rather to stem from the dynamics of the social system of science, and in particular from the problems that are related to the norm of disinterestedness.

Applied research is, by definition, research intended to assist in the solution of practical problems. Inasmuch as it is only happenstance when the solution to a practical problem will have important consequences for a body of generalized knowledge, the scientist must generally choose whether he wishes his work to be of interest to those who want it first to solve an immediate problem or to those who are more concerned with its contribution to generalized knowledge. At the heart of the distinction is the question: Which audience is more important to the researcher? To recall the metaphor suggested by Shepard, quoted in Chapter Two, the scientist who tries to be both "pure" and "applied" is like an actor trying to play simultaneously before two separate audiences with different tastes.

The audience for applied research obviously cannot be expected to reward the scientist with competent response, for typically it is made up of nonscientists. The nonscientist may of course appreciate a solution that works, but he is not competent to appreciate the creativity that went into it; at best, his only direct expression of appreciation is gratitude. And because, normatively, the scientist is supposed to want above all competent response to his work, it is assumed by other scientists that he would not ordinarily choose to engage in research that is unlikely to be of interest to his professional colleagues unless he were more interested in the commodity the nonscientist can bestow.

This commodity is of course money, received by the researcher either as salary or as a consultant's fee. In interviews with scientists in industry, I have occasionally heard one say spontaneously and rather wryly that he had "sold his soul for gold"—and in the normative sense this statement is true. I am fairly sure that such statements were an indirect way for these men to indicate to me, a representative of "basic" research, their acquaintance with the norms of science rather than an expression of deeply felt guilt. Nevertheless, the statement has a certain significance in terms of our interests here. It indicates an awareness on the part of these men that they are subject to the expectation that they will support the reward system of science, even if they are not personally motivated to do so.

It may appear that the "defection" of a scientist from basic research (or at least from the atmosphere of basic research in which he probably received his training) to applied research (a position in industry or government) seems to contradict my earlier arguments about the importance of the desire to be creative in the motivation of scientists. I think it does not, but a brief discussion of the question is in order. There are two possible explanations of why a scientist may want to engage in applied research; and one explanation, which is basically situational, of why he may have to engage in it. First, it may be that the desire to create is less strong or enduring in some men than in others, so that the "kick" in carrying out basic research diminishes and the man is less resistant to the higher salaries typically paid by industry. Second, it is quite possible that a man may wish to be "concretely" creative, to produce "things that work" rather than abstract ideas on paper; such an interest is more likely to be satisfied in applied research than in basic, even though the size of the technically competent audience may be drastically reduced.

Third, and perhaps the most important reason for entering "applied" research, is the fact that the job-market in any particular year may force many scientists into this area when they would have preferred to remain in an academic setting. Thereafter, a kind of career inertia (preference for the known and hesitance to give up one's current standard of living and accrued employment benefits) would seem often to hold them in applied research even when basic research opportunities are again developed. In applied research, also, there is often the chance to "bootleg" some pure research into one's work, so that one will have materials of general interest to the scientific community as well as to the employer.[11]

It is in the distinction between basic and applied research that the norm of disinterestedness is tested most directly. Does the researcher value the money he receives from his employers more than the competent response he can receive from his colleagues? With certain exceptions, his apparent answer to this question is to be found in his choice of employment. If he works in industry, he is assumed to be more sensitive to money than to recognition, whereas if he is located in a university, the opposite is assumed to be true. In recent years this generalization has been challenged by situations like that existing in the electronics industry, where basic research in solid-state physics has been vigorously encouraged because of the relatively short time required to turn basic discovery into practical application. The same may be true in some parts of the ethical drug industry and in certain chemical industries. Yet from the point of view of the basic scientists in the universities, these are only exceptions to the general rule. They are reacting to the principle of the thing, the assumption that a man who is paid directly for his research is not likely to produce findings that will be of general interest to other scientists and so is probably not concerned with his colleagues' evaluations of his work.

Inasmuch as less than one third of all those in America who can be classified as scientists are in the universities, their only defense against this apparently massive violation of the norm of disinterestedness is to point to the moral failure involved. That applied researchers show an awareness of how they are viewed, and sometimes agree with this view, seems to show the potency of the norm. In terms of social systems, the compromising of different exchange systems is a moral wrong, and this wrong is specified here in the violation of disinterestedness.

At the motivational level, I think we can explain the tendency of basic scientists to look down upon applied scientists as a defense of the availability of competent response. It appears obvious that when a man is working on something that is not interesting to a colleague, the chances for technically competent communication between them are diminished. Neither will be able to evaluate the other's work, nor may they be interested in doing so. This situation is, of course, endemic in the continual subdivision of science into more and more specialty areas, but when the researcher's problems are posed by nonscientists, they have even less likelihood of being relevant to each other because they do not stem from the same body of generalized knowledge. Within basic science, where the emphasis is upon generalization rather than specification, there is reason to expect that through the office of theory findings in one area may be seen eventually to have consequences for work in other areas. There is apparently less emphasis upon theory in applied science; when something is found that "works," less attention is paid to establishing its theoretical importance or to exploring the various other conditions under which it will and will not work, unless there is apparent practical reason for doing so.

If competent response is to be generally available within science, there must be widespread agreement among scientists as to what constitutes valuable work and how it is to be evaluated. Such agreement depends upon there being a shared body of knowledge and theory that contains within itself implicit directions for the further extension of knowledge. Without such a common universe of discourse, the problem of collectively identifying important questions and of evaluating the work of individual scientists would become virtually impossible. To the extent that scientists deny the importance of this universe of discourse through working on problems that do not originate in it, they are seen to be threatening the very conditions under which competent response may continue to be obtained. It is thus not so much the validity of response to creativity that is in danger as it is the availability of this response. Hagstrom's discussion (1965, pp. 226–236) of such a situation in mathematics, under the heading, "Specialization without Integration: Anomy," is an excellent review of some of the consequences of the lack of a common universe of discourse within a basic science.

There would be, however, disadvantages to a completely closed universe of discourse, and they are often pointed out by applied scientists. Such a body of knowledge would not only determine in advance the important questions to be answered, but would determine also the kinds of answers that would be acceptable. Such complete isolation of scientific activity from outside influences might lead eventually to a kind of scholasticism in which smaller and smaller questions assume greater and greater importance. The field in which practitioners feel that they have nothing left to do but work out the next decimal place is held up as an example of such a situation.

The dependence of the applied researcher upon questions from outside of science—from industry, agriculture, and government—means that his findings are unlikely to fill strategic gaps in theory or in empirical knowledge, even though he works with the same existing knowledge and research methods that the basic scientist uses. This situation, too, if carried to extremes, would be harmful to the continued existence of science. For short periods, as in wartime, scientists may be almost wholly devoted to applied research, but their ability to work effectively during such relatively limited periods cannot be assumed to disprove the contention that over the long run such a collective focus upon problems of application would be harmful to the social organization of science.

In generating and selecting questions for research, science must thus seek continually for a balance between too much dependence on an inbred universe of theoretical discourse on the one hand and too much dependence upon external sources on the other. In the former case there is the danger of ignoring problems that might lead to important advances in theory and knowledge, whereas in the latter the maintenance of the entire social system would be jeopardized. And there is information at hand that supports the contention that communication and contact between basic and applied research can be extremely valuable. If the previous argument is valid, it would seem that a judicious admixture of the two points of view—a solid commitment to the development of an organized body of knowledge combined with considerable exposure to questions that do not originate in this body of knowledge—will promote the most effective advancement of knowledge.

Ben-David, in analyzing the development of bacteriology and of psychoanalysis, points out that the pioneers in both fields were men who had originally been what we could call basic scientists but who "were driven by personal or professional reasons to solve practical problems."[12] Semmelweiss, Pasteur, Lister, and Koch were all men who had come from academic backgrounds in which there was an accepted body of theory, and, in the course of attacking practical problems (anthrax, fermentation, cowpox, surgical and delivery-room mortality), they achieved advances that could not have come from previous theory alone. Similarly, Freud had been "a scholar engaged in the kind of medical research that was the usual preparation for an academic career in German and Austrian medicine"[13] when he began his investigation of hysteria.

The advantageous effects of exposing a scientist to questions from outside his own background and frame of reference is also supported by the findings of Pelz and his associates (1953 pp. 36–42). In studies carried out at a large government research institute, Pelz found that a scientist's "mean performance" as judged by his colleagues and superiors was definitely enhanced by frequent contact with colleagues whose interests differed from the scientist's own, in this case, differences in allegiance to science or to the local organization.

These examples seem to parallel on a smaller scale the point made earlier about the origins of research questions for science as a whole. Too many questions from "outside" will disrupt the universe of discourse upon which the social system of science is based, whereas too few will reduce its rate of advance, limiting unduly the types of questions to which scientists will address themselves.

The advantages to be gained through continued, close contact between basic and applied scientists are obvious. But so long as the dual needs of science continue to require occasionally conflicting behavior on the part of its members—on the one hand to protect the integrity of the system in which competent response is generally available and on the other to push ahead as rapidly as possible (that is, to continue being creative) in investigating the physical and social universe—the presence of some hostility between the two groups may be expected to continue.

Perhaps the use of scientists as consultants is the best answer to the problem of how to keep them exposed to practical problems while maintaining their major commitment to basic science. Their main base of operations would remain in the universities but at the same time part-time work on the problems of industry or government may keep their horizons as broad as possible. It may be that the acceptance of contract research from industry and government to be carried out in the universities can perform the same function even more effectively, although the consequences of this arrangement for other aspects of the university may make it a less satisfactory over-all answer.

This discussion of the distinction between basic and applied research and of the social-structural concommitants of its origins within the social system of science has perhaps gone into more detail than is necessary to establish my main point. Yet the topic is of particular interest to scientists, and I have felt it necessary to discuss the functions as well as the dysfunctions of applied research for the scientific enterprise as a whole, since often its relation to basic research has been thought of primarily in negative terms. It should be noted that the social structure of science is relatively simple in comparison with that of other social systems, so that we can see its central dynamics with greater clarity. The covert hostility between basic and applied research is an important example of these dynamics, and it is quite possible that as the scientific community becomes larger and more complex, the issue will disappear and be replaced by other internal conflicts of quite a different nature.

Having seen how the norm of disinterestedness serves to maintain the autonomy of science as a social system by discouraging the substitution of other commodities for that of competent response and how scientists are motivated to support this norm because of their concern for maintaining the validity and the availability of competent response, we can proceed now to a consideration of the next set of problems. These center about the norm of organized scepticism.

Problems Involving Organized Scepticism

As this norm has been defined in Chapter Five, it covers not only the scientist's obligation to provide competent response to the work of other scientists but also his obligation to be sensitive to the comments and criticism that others make of his own work. He must provide the commodity that others seek and at the same time he must seek it himself. The function of this norm for the social system of science is to prevent the use of self-generated rewards as the motivation for research, since this practice would render all internal controls ineffective and thus result in the disintegration of science as a social structure. Further, it would, through allowing each scientist to be the final judge of the validity and significance of his own work, greatly weaken the organization of the body of knowledge with which science is concerned; this in turn would mean the undermining of scientists' sense of the objective reality of this body of knowledge and, thus, would do away eventually with the very context in which creativity has meaning. In terms both of the social organization of science and of the complex nature of creativity, then, the prohibition against the scientist's providing competent response for himself is of the utmost importance.

THE GENIUS AND THE CRACKPOT

The norm of organized scepticism may be violated in two ways: through failure to respond appropriately to the contributions of others, and through failure to be properly attentive to others' responses to one's own contributions. The difficulty that arises when something exceptionally novel is presented to science, that is, the problem of distinguishing between the crackpot and the genius who is just "ahead of his time" is thus compounded, for both of these violations may be cited in each case. The person who keeps insisting that his work is valid and valuable, long after it has been rejected by others, is accused not only of being wrong in the technical sense but also of refusing to be appropriately sensitive to the criticism of others. He, however, usually claims that his work *is* correct and that his critics are not really giving him *competent* response. The question is not simply whether the work is correct or incorrect but whether one party to the dispute or the other has in some way violated the norm of organized scepticism; the dispute becomes a moral as well as a technical matter.

In point of fact, it is usually those who claim that the individual in question did not pay sufficient attention to criticism who turn out to have been right. Despite the many cases that may be cited from the history of science of genius going unrecognized and unappreciated for years, the number of actual crackpots whose "contributions" have rightly been rejected by scientists is probably greater by at least an order of magnitude.

It is always difficult, of course, to determine just how much attention a scientist has really paid to criticism of his work, and whenever he rejects it, his critic is almost bound to feel that it has not been given adequate consideration. Normatively, therefore, a scientist is expected to answer criticism with rational discussion rather than with silence. Here, the norm of rationalism —the requirement that a scientist communicate with his colleagues in terms of shared standards of reasoning and of proof— may be invoked, but this norm seems more important in making the original contributor put his contribution into a form intelligible to his intended audience. For our purposes, we shall look at the preemptory rejection of criticism as a violation of organized scepticism.

The ideal resolution of an argument between two or more scientists over the validity of evidence is to replicate the research, and in the case of an argument over the interpretation of data it is their agreement on what would be the "crucial experiment" to provide the kind of additional information that would decide the matter, under the terms of the discussion, in favor of one interpretation or the other. Particularly in the latter case, but sometimes also in the former, this is an *ideal* (as opposed to real) solution, because, for various reasons, such resolutions may be extremely difficult to achieve. This difficulty may be due to the expense or even the impossibility of replicating the research (for instance, a nation-wide survey or an ethnology of a now extinct tribe, or data on a particular eclipse or from an inaccessible high-energy accelerator), or to the failure of the critic to have an alternate explanation of the phenomena he is questioning, or to the fact that the critic is employing a different criterion of validity or significance from that which the contributor used. In any case, when an acceptable resolution to the problem cannot be found, or agreement cannot be reached concerning how it might be resolved, nonscientific factors will come into play and the way is open to complaints about violations of "accepted practice"—in this case, of organized scepticism.

When there is agreement among most scientists who have some competence in the area of discussion that the person criticized has not "played by the rules," that he has either ignored a legitimate criticism or he has responded to it in unacceptable terms, then that person may be "defined out" of the group. He has either violated the norm of organized scepticism through being insensitive to criticism, or else he is less familiar with the rules of the game than had been assumed; in either case, continued scientific contact with him will seem less valuable to the others and they will pay less attention to both his contributions and his criticisms in the future. Particularly with the increasing trend towards dependence upon informal communication within science (to be discussed in the next chapter), which means that the frontier of a field of research cannot be known simply through reading the published literature, such ostracism can be highly effective in excluding a man almost totally from active participation in the ongoing work of his field. When the man continues to defend the goodness of his work in the face of these "negative sanctions," the others may eventually have to decide whether or not he should be branded a crackpot.

This decision, however, cannot be made solely on the absolute grounds of whether the man is correct or incorrect. In many instances, there is no way to determine this, or even to determine whether a new theoretical framework might be more or less useful than the one currently accepted. Judgment instead must be made on the basis of how well the new contribution "fits" current knowledge as a refinement or extension of it. This situation, I suggest, is inherent in the nature of creativity in science, for, as was pointed out in Chapter Four, to be creative an idea, be it scientific or artistic, must stand in some understandable relationship to the current state of the art or body of knowledge. If the terms in which a contribution represents an extension of current knowledge cannot be perceived by those evaluating it, by definition it cannot be accepted as creative. Instead, it will be seen at best as irrelevant to the body of knowledge, and at worst as an attempt to insert incorrect materials into the established body of knowledge.

This may be illustrated by a brief analogy. If scientists are engaged in enlarging a clearing in the woods—of exploring more of the vast store of knowledge that remains to be discovered —and someone suddenly claims to know of a clearing in a different part of the woods, he will be ignored unless he can show the others *how he got there.* After all, there are only certain ways that a man can move through the woods, and if this fellow says he got there by flying or by being carried by angels, no one will believe that he was ever there at all. In science, similarly, if the discoverer of something new cannot "lead" others to it by means they can accept, they are not likely to welcome his discovery at all. Instead, they may suspect him of seeking professional recognition through illegitimate means and damn him the more for his egotism than for his technical weaknesses.

As was pointed out above, it would be dangerous to the organization of knowledge if findings that cannot somehow be related to the established body of knowledge were to be too freely admitted into this body. And if its organization were to be severely disrupted, the standards by which significant creativity could be measured would be drastically weakened and a situation of anomie would result; there would neither be basis for selecting problems of particular importance, nor standards for the assessment of the validity of new findings, and scientists would lose the framework of meaning in which their work assumes its value to them.

For very good reason, then, scientists tend to be conservative in accepting new discoveries. Only when a contribution is "certified," that is, acceptable to other scientists under the canons of proof they share, will it be welcomed. A contribution must be an understandable extension of knowledge, and if it fails to meet this test, either because others simply cannot understand its relation to current knowledge or because it seems to fly in the face of accepted standards of reasoning, it will be rejected and its author's credentials as a scientist will become suspect. This means that a scientist who is so far ahead of his colleagues that they cannot understand how he arrived at his conclusions or why they are important will be treated in the same way that a hollow-earth theorist is treated. In both cases, their contributions seem to threaten the integration of knowledge because they are irrelevant or inconsistent with the rest of the body of knowledge.

This is of course an idealized picture of the situation, for no field of science has a perfectly integrated body of knowledge and there will always be exceptions to the rule that states knowledge that cannot be meaningfully related to accepted knowledge will be rejected. Such a rule, in fact, would be harmful to science, for it would close the door to criticism of previously accepted knowledge and would block off all but the barest introduction of new findings not expected on the basis of previous knowledge.

Science, though, is geared to the average scientist rather than to its outstanding geniuses. A crackpot may be unable to provide acceptable reasoning as to how he reached his conclusions, and a genius may be impatient at having to provide them, but both are subject to the requirement that they demonstrate to their colleagues how they did it, and both are subject to the same penalties when they ignore this obligation.

By definition, the crackpot will be unable to do this. For the genius, two pathways lie open, and both are amply illustrated in the history of science. The first is to take pains in marking one's path so that others will be able to follow it; Newton's painstaking labors in translating his *Principia* into geometrical proofs, after he had solved the problems originally through the use of his "fluxions" or the calculus, is an illustration. The second method requires more patience and fortitude; it is the method of foregoing acceptance by one's colleagues until one has been able to train a new generation of students who are able to understand what one is doing; Freud's training of his followers, despite their tendencies to break with him later on, is an example of this method. In the field of sociology, I would venture to guess that

Talcott Parsons has had to follow this second method also.

When the genius has failed to follow one or the other of these courses, or when for other reasons his work is rejected by his colleagues,[14] he is helpless and must wait simply for the passage of time in hope that he will be vindicated. When such vindication finally comes about, science will often experience a collective sense of guilt that it had so maltreated one of its members and will worry a good deal about why it was that his work was originally rejected. The fruits of such self-examination may be seen in the recent furor over the work of Dr. Immanuel Velikovsky.[15] Perhaps the point to be made here is that such mistakes as the rejection of Thomas Young's wave theory of light[16] or the unfair treatment of Velikovsky's work—regardless of the ultimate decision on the correctness of the latter—are as natural, given the social structure of science, as is the rejection of genuine crackpots. This is not simply to say that scientists are less perfect than their ideals claim for them, or that their human pettiness and irrationality account entirely for their occasional rejection of work later found to be highly creative and meaningful. Rather, it argues that scientific truth is, *for the moment*, what is accepted by the majority of scientists in a given area and that its acceptance is based upon its relation to other truths rather than upon its absolute, independent merit.

Nor does this analysis really suggest that science must always operate at the level of the lowest common denominator and, thus, that scientific progress must always be slow. A crucial feature of the scientific enterprise is that progress depends primarily upon empirical demonstration and logical consistency rather than upon rhetorical argument, and so long as there is agreement upon the rules of demonstration, the lowest common denominator can be raised a good deal in a very short time. At worst, the opponents of a new theory are usually unsuccessful in recruiting new members to their camp, and as they retire from the field, there is little but the empirical evidence, handled according to accepted standards of proof, to help or hinder the new theory from becoming the new common denominator. Barber quotes Max Planck on this point: "A new scientific truth does not triumph by convincing its opponents and making them see the light, but rather because its opponents eventually die, and a new generation grows up that is familiar with it."[17]

The central point here is that the inability of the scientific community at any given time to distinguish between an idea that is entirely wrong and an idea that may be viewed as brilliant at some later date is not an intellectual failure that might be corrected but is rather an inherently insoluble problem. The cultural base upon which science is built, the organized body of certified knowledge to which scientists refer in their current work, determines whether a contribution will be accepted easily or whether its author must fight and suffer to obtain acceptance for his work (regardless of his final success or failure). To change the rules so that no one need struggle for the acceptance of his work would fatally injure the social structure that is so important to him. I am thus suggesting that whereas it is important for scientists to assess the amount of "unfair play" that may have been involved in the initial rejection of a valuable contribution, as they have, for example, done in the issue of *The American Behavioral Scientist* concerned with "The Politics of Science and Dr. Velikovsky," it is futile to hope that such occurrences as the rejection of Mendel's work can ever be eliminated.

"Fair play," too, in the absolute sense, cannot be expected. Despite historical instances where this has occurred it is not reasonable to expect that one scientist will devote himself to establishing a theoretical context in order to give someone *else's* contribution meaning and importance; if the contributor himself has not done this, he has no real right to claim later on that his work had been treated unfairly. This is to say that the contributor is responsible not only for finding "a truth" but for making it meaningful to his colleagues in terms of the body of knowledge with which they are mutually concerned, and his rejection when he fails to do this may be traced ultimately to his colleagues' interest in maintaining a universe of discourse in which creativity is meaningful and may be evaluated.

AUTHORITY AND ADEQUATE RESPONSE

Two lesser problems in the social structure of science that involve organized scepticism, neither of which constitutes a serious threat to the community as a whole, may be mentioned briefly. One is the substitution of authority for personal judgment: The individual violates his responsibility for evaluating the work of others by accepting a third party's judgment of it. In this case, clearly, complete fidelity to the norm is impossible, so that the problem is not one of eliminating the practice but of holding it down to an acceptable level. The other problem concerns the adequacy of one's response to the work of others, especially the questions of how soon one should respond and of how critical the response should be.

Authority. The first problem arises from the scientist's lack of time to scrutinize all new materials that may be relevant to his own interests; consequently he must depend to some extent upon his colleagues' evaluations of others' work. The danger here lies in allowing the "chain of authority" to grow too long. If the scientist who accepts an evaluation is more than two or three steps removed from the initial evaluator, the chances that the former will act on the basis of an incorrect evaluation may increase beyond a tolerable level. For instance, if Smith accepts Brown's word, which he got from Jones, who heard from Johnson that Harrison's article is a good treatment of the relationship between X and Y, Smith may be unable to gauge Johnson's trustworthiness and thus may be accepting the word of an incompetent judge. Too, the "degeneration" of information as it passes from one man to another may seriously bias what Smith hears about Harrison's work.

Further, yielding to the widely-felt pressure to "keep up with the literature," a scientist may occasionally feign acquaintance with a book or article in order to maintain the appearance of living up to this requirement. This is a sort of "academic gamesmanship" that, among other things, contributes to a high level of anxiety among graduate students about their personal competence in mastering the literature, and a scientist's uncritical acceptance of another's uninformed "judgment" can have unfortunate consequences.

Even so, the scientist must depend upon his colleagues for assistance in staying abreast of his field. Because the scientific community's defense against gross violations of organized scepticism is generally effective, that is, a scientist is not "forgiven" when his own error is based upon his innocent acceptance of another's error, the dilemma generated here must be resolved in some way by every working scientist. There are two common solutions. The first is increasing specialization, whereby the scientist is able to define so narrowly the type of information relevant to his interests that he actually *can* be personally responsible for evaluating everything of this type that appears. It would seem that the desire to obey the norm of organized scepticism is thus an important pressure in producing specialization within science; this tendency is countered only by the scientist's concern with generalized knowledge, which forces him to pay attention to the relationship between his specialized subject and the broader field of which it is a part.

The second solution is the development of small, informal groups of scientists who trust each other's judgment. Certain problems are inherent here, however, inasmuch as such groups are ordinarily made up of men who are at work on the same topic and the competition among them for priority may threaten the assumption of mutual trust necessary for such groups to operate successfully. But because the group also constitutes the major audience for the creativity of each member, all are concerned with the maintenance of the group as well as with trying to outdo each other in achievement. The result seems generally to be that the members who stay with such groups are those who can tolerate a relatively high level of tension in their relations with the other members and so tend to be the "stronger" men in the field, even if only because their high need to be creative forces them to endure the tensions characteristic of such groups.

Adequate Response. A final violation of organized scepticism is the failure to respond "adequately" to the work of others. This may be the failure to respond at all—and excessively late response is a lesser crime of the same sort—or it may be failure to respond objectively. The former is more clearly a crime of omission, so it is difficult to bring formal criticism to bear upon a scientist for this sort of violation of the norm; he may gradually acquire an informal reputation as being a "poor correspondent" or as being "uninterested in the work of others," but such characteristics are not grounds for righteous public denunciation of him. At worst, such behavior on his part may result in his receiving fewer communications from his colleagues and thus in being partially excluded from the "center" of work in his field.

The scientist who always responds to his colleagues' work with generous praise will find eventually that his own reputation begins to suffer. Here he fails in not being sceptical rather than in not responding at all, and whereas someone may be hard put to criticize a man who praises his work, his private estimate of the man's abilities may well decline when the man's continual lack of substantive criticism becomes apparent. Similarly, the man who can never say anything good about others' work will be disliked. It is perhaps better for a scientist to be too critical in his responses rather than too accepting, but because most scientists have a considerable emotional stake in their work, they may become quite unhappy unless the good points about their work are noted along with the weaknesses.

As a result, a number of techniques have been developed to enable the critic to take the sting out of his criticisms while still keeping them intact. One of these is to characterize a poor work as "needed exploration," thereby indicating approval of the author's intent even though his substantive results may be torn to shreds. Another is to indicate the various audiences that will appreciate a work, even if they are not composed of those whose opinions are presumably most important to the author. These practices and variations on them seem generally to be attempts to make clear the distinction between an evaluation of the scientist as an individual and the evaluation of a specific work bearing his name. When this is successful, critical response to a man's contribution may be objective and even quite destructive, but his intellectual and emotional integrity are specifically exempted from such criticism. Thus, with varying degrees of success, scientists are able to obey the norm of organized scepticism without allowing their actions to become destructive of the motivations that underlie research.

Of course, when the critic is anonymous, such gestures of goodwill may be omitted. The occasional complaints heard about the use of anonymous readers to evaluate articles submitted to journals seem to focus essentially upon how anonymity provides license for *ad hominem* criticism and undisguised hostility. The need to keep separate the goodness of the man and the goodness of his creative product is clearly illustrated here, although the reason for keeping reviewers anonymous is presumably to protect them from the compulsion to be too generous in their evaluations, as well as from "political" retaliation.

It is apparent, then, that the requirement that scientists be "strictly honest" in their response to the work of others comes into conflict at several points with the *social* needs of the scientific community, needs rooted in the nature of creativity and in the motivation of scientists. Scientists must give competent response to each other, but the questions of what constitutes *competent* response and what is the proper form in which it should be cast are a continuing source of anxiety and controversy, and the modes of resolving these problems are important in shaping many of the folkways that have developed within science.

Problems Involving Communality

The norm of communality concerns the scientist's obligation to share his work with others, not only in response to specific requests but as a general practice, regardless of whether or not he knows of individuals who will be interested in it. In a very basic sense, this norm affirms the independent existence of the body of knowledge to which the scientist is contributing; it asks that the scientist make his work a part of this general body of knowledge by making it generally available through publication. The actual behavior of scientists, however, is influenced by several aspects of the social structure of science that detract from the full implementation of this norm.

SECRECY

The most obvious impediment to its implementation stems from the fact that knowledge is power, and to keep information out of another's hands is to maintain one's own superiority in the area in question. Certainly the imposition of governmental security restrictions upon the communication of scientific information is the most obvious case in point. Because such information was and is of potential value to "the enemy," whoever that may be, the norm of secrecy in the name of the nation, or even of the company, has been invoked to override the norm of communality. Beginning in the 1930s with the development of radar, certain parts of the scientific community became more and more intimately acquainted with government-imposed restrictions upon the dissemination of information. This is not the place to go into the story of wartime security measures and the rapid disenchantment of scientists with such measures after 1945, culminating in the Oppenheimer hearings during the McCarthy era, except to take note of the fact that while during the war scientists seemed generally satisfied that stringent security measures were necessary, a broader appreciation of their potentially disastrous consequences for science after the war led to increasing resistance to them.

To accept at face value the scientists' arguments against secrecy would, however, be to see only a part of the picture. These arguments are generally couched in terms of "efficiency," of the waste involved in forcing scientists to repeat work that others have already carried out because reports of this work are unavailable; this point, indeed, makes economic sense. I would suggest, though, a more immediate reason for the dislike of security restrictions: they prevent the scientist from letting his colleagues know what he has done. To be sure, a scientist is not held by his colleagues to be violating a norm when his failure to communicate his findings is involuntary, so we cannot say that security regulations injure a scientist's reputation directly, but to the extent that they prevent him from participating in the social system of science, they do serious injury to his motivation and self-image.

After all, the scientist generally wants his colleagues' responses to his creative products, and policies that prevent his making these products public serve at the same time to prevent his receiving such response. But he is unable to complain on these grounds, for, as we have seen, there are strong blocks to his admission of his desire for professional recognition. Security restrictions are thus disliked not so much because they prevent a scientist from learning what *others* have done as because they prevent him from telling others what *he* has done. The enforced violation of communality is, indeed, deleterious to the progress of science, but of more immediate importance to the scientist is the fact that he is effectively removed from participation in the exchange system through being denied the opportunity to receive response to his work.

Data are not available to test this interpretation, so far as I am aware; several scientists I have interviewed have suggested to me that one excellent measure of scientific motivation would be a man's answer to the question, "Would you want to be a scientist if you had to publish all your work anonymously?" The obvious answer, according to my informants, would be a resounding "No!" and I think that such a situation, in which the scientist works anonymously, is roughly analogous to that existing when a scientist's work is "classified" and kept secret. To be sure, he probably has a few colleagues who know his work, but their awareness of it does not really give it the objective existence it would have if it were published and made a part of the public record.

Here again, then, I am proposing that a "social problem" in science is a problem not so much because it threatens to hamper the general "advancement of knowledge" but because it interferes very directly with the exchange system upon which science is founded and which directly affects the scientist's motivation.

Voluntary refusals to share information constitute a different type of problem, if only because they are entirely intrascience rather than a conflict between science and the larger society. This may mean either the refusal to share findings, usually because one is unsure of their validity (whether this uncertainty is realistic or not) and wishes to examine them further, or the refusal to share the details of how one's findings were reached. The former is obviously a more serious problem, particularly when a pathological secretiveness delays the publication of good, useful work, but the latter type probably leads to more controversy. Here, the obvious implication of a scientist's refusal to tell others the details of his research methods is that he does not want others to replicate his work, and thus that he may be a crackpot rather than simply misanthropically reluctant to share his work with others. As Gruenberger points out, "The charlatan and the boob are both intrinsically opposed to a search for the truth; the last thing they want is public verifiability and controlled experimentation."[18]

The refusal to share the details of one's work, when not

motivated by fear of the exposure of scientific fraud, may be due, as I have noted, to a pathological reluctance to "commit" oneself to possible error. The more desperate a scientist is to be creative and the more deeply he is involved in his work, the more he will identify himself with it and the more ready he will be to interpret criticism of it as criticism of himself. For such a scientist, publication means the exposure of his very heart and mind to many people who are not likely to be sympathetic; the threat of being met with hostility can make the prospect of publication quite frightening to him and he may avoid this by refusing to present his findings at all. He would, however, *like* to make them public, and presumably experiences considerable internal conflict over the matter.

This anxiety is due not to the man's sense that he is violating a scientific norm but to the conflict between his own deep need for affirmation of the meaningfulness of his work and his fear that this will not be forthcoming from his colleagues. Although his behavior may be interpreted as the outcome of a conflict between the norm of communality and the norm of organized scepticism (in the sense that he is responsible for the goodness of his work), I suggest that the problem may be more effectively explained through reference to the nature of the desire to create and its personal importance to the individual.

A more "normal" reason for refusing to share one's work is the fear that to reveal a half-completed project will enable someone else to complete it more quickly, get it into print first, and acquire priority for himself. A continuing problem for the researcher, therefore, is that of how soon to let his colleagues know of his work in progress. Because the establishment of priority depends upon publication generally (except in the special case to be discussed below), and publication ordinarily requires the presentation of data, the scientist who has not yet obtained all the information he wants, but is fairly sure of what it will be, may well be reluctant to tell a colleague what he is working on. Particularly when a scientist has other responsibilities, such as teaching or administration, that prevent him from working as rapidly as he would wish, he may hesitate to give others the chance to "scoop" him.[19]

From this point of view, the man is perfectly justified in withholding information about his current research until he is ready to publish it. But it is true also that incompletely worked out ideas—speculative hypotheses, interpretations of partial data, even untried research techniques—can be useful for scientists, other than the originators of these ideas, working on other projects, and the person who is refused access to work in progress may well complain that the over-all progress of science is being hampered by his colleague's refusal to share his ideas. He will have special justification for his complaint if work in progress is withheld because its originator suspects it will demonstrate that others are working on the basis of faulty conceptualizations or incorrect data, for the moral problem becomes more serious when a man purposely allows his colleagues to follow a false trail until he has gathered sufficient data to demonstrate his own correctness in the matter. Here, he has not only withheld information, but by his silence has implicitly encouraged others to continue working along lines that he has reason to think will *not* yield them any priority at all.

There is no simple rubric, then, for deciding how soon or under what circumstances a scientist should tell his colleagues about his current research activities. To share it with all comers from the moment of inception would be to diminish his chances to "profit" by his own work, whereas to allow him to guard it until it is ready for publication would be to undermine the mutual trust among scientists that is necessary if they are to continue their mutual support of science's exchange-system. How the problem is resolved will be to a considerable extent a matter of the scientist's position vis-á-vis his colleagues and of the state of the field in which he is working.

For instance, the "hotter" a field is, the more rapidly advances in knowledge are being made, the more likely it is that the main work is being done by scientists who participate a great deal in small, informal groups. This situation develops in fast-moving fields in part because of the "publication lag" and in part because such advances usually involve comparatively basic reconceptualization of the field that has not yet had time to become established and widely accepted. Informal communication networks are thus the only type of structure that can facilitate the scientist's work and assure him of a competent audience for his creativity. In such cases, where scientists tend to know one another as individuals, there should be less reluctance to divulge preliminary findings and hypotheses since priority is assured by personal knowledge rather than simply through publication. The man who tries to "steal" another's ideas in order to publish first will be subject to his colleagues' criticism because they know who had the ideas first. In other words, the more likely one's priority can be supported by others' personal knowledge of who had an idea first, the more willing he will be to share his preliminary findings and interpretations.

Conversely, the more "quiet" a field is, the less likelihood there is that the men working in it will be involved in informal communication among themselves. By definition, advances will be less frequent, priority will be scarce, and when there is both higher motivation to seek priority and less chance that some form of plagiary will be detected, it is reasonable to suppose that scientists will be more reluctant to share informally their work in progress with others until it is ready for publication.

Thus, the social-structural characteristics of a field of science will have a major influence upon how strictly the norm of communality is interpreted by scientists in that field. The characteristics with greatest reference to that norm are the ones determining how scientists may best pattern their interrelations so that the allocation of competent response to creativity may be carried out on a "fair" basis, giving all participants a roughly equal chance to acquire it in return for their own work. So, once more, the underlying importance of maintaining a structure in which motivation will be sustained may be seen operating in this case as well as in the others that have been discussed.

ACCESS TO THE ATTENTION OF OTHERS

Finally, there is the situation in which the norm of communality is violated not by an individual's voluntary withholding information but by his being blocked from receiving the appropriate attention of other scientists. Most obvious here is his being blocked from publication, for publication is almost the *sine qua non* of participation in the social system of science. Actually, because "the literature" includes obscure as well as major journals and the books of minor as well as major publishers, the question here is usually *which* publications reject a man's work rather than that of whether he can publish at all. Once an article is published anywhere, the author generally can obtain reprints and send them to the men in his field whose opinions of the work he would like to receive. Many would-be contributors to science have undoubtedly met a series of editors who told them in effect, "Your work is interesting but it does not fall within the sphere of my journal's interests," and have either been discouraged or else had to seek publication in tiny, obscure journals. Another response to this frustration is to establish a new journal that will accept the article, although this would generally be one of the later steps in the process of establishing a new area of specialization within science.

This problem is of course intimately related to the matter of the distinction between the genius and the crackpot, inasmuch as the usual response to a crackpot is to deny him opportunity to publish his work. Here, however, the emphasis is more upon the power relationships involved rather than upon the substantive goodness of the material submitted for publication. Barber's famous paper noted earlier, on "Resistance by Scientists to Scientific Discovery" (in Barber and Hirsch, 1962) concentrates almost entirely upon cases in which sound contributions were rejected on essentially non-scientific grounds such as religious opinions, status differences, the guarding of personal reputations, or the hostilities among different schools of thought. And he deals almost entirely with cases in which a contribution was published but then failed to receive adequate attention from other scientists, for obviously, he could not study those potential contributions that were entirely rejected and thus disappeared. However, we must be concerned here with the denial of access to publication, because the problem of getting others to pay attention to one's published work seems to be more directly related to the norm of organized scepticism, or of getting others to provide competent response to a contribution.

This is, as I have mentioned, mainly a matter of who holds the power to accept or reject a contribution on behalf of a journal and of what standards he employs. When a rejected contributor is given a copy of the reviewer's comments, should he disagree with these comments, he may legitimately complain that the reviewer was wrong and ask that the paper be reviewed again; he has no assurance, however, that he can obtain "justice" in this way. Hagstrom (1965, p. 18) cites an interesting example of such a case.

In the social structure of science, then, a certain degree of arbitrary power is operating, which is countered only by the multiplicity of journals and by the opportunity to begin the publication of new journals. This power is rarely questioned, not only because it is rarely used viciously or high-handedly but also because the strength of the egalitarian ethos within science, which has promoted the development of many techniques that facilitate the mobilization of countervailing forces, requires generally that consensus be obtained before power is employed. The proliferation of committees in academia is a direct consequence of the scholar's preference for consensus over authority, and both the values of those who could use power arbitrarily within science and the structure within which they must operate ensure that its employment is usually held to a minimum.

Thus, although denial of the opportunity to obey the norm of communality is in principle a problem within science, I know of no evidence suggesting that it is actually a major problem. There are of course degrees of relative ease of access to channels of communication, depending partly upon patterns of personal friendship and of institutional affiliation, and these seem mainly to operate in favor of the older, more established men. Despite the feeling that all scientists should be equal and that it is inappropriate to gauge a man's work on the basis of his past accomplishments rather than upon its immediate merits, I think it is impossible to deny that a man with an established reputation will have an easier time getting his work accepted for publication than will a younger, relatively unknown man.

Given the fact of limited space in journals, particularly for the younger man, he may have cause to feel that the cards are to some extent stacked against him, the more so because "invited" articles sometimes occupy some of this space. Yet these "odds" do serve as a kind of filter that assures that only the better of the younger men will achieve reputations and thus join the group of "established" scientists. Further, the relative ease with which an older man can get into print may mean that a new idea, which would have been rejected if contributed by an unknown, can indeed if presented by the established scientist be published and thus added to the literature. Barber (in Barber and Hirsch, 1962, p. 552) mentions such an incident in the life of Lord Rayleigh. A younger man who is championed by a senior scientist may similarly have better luck in attracting the attention of his colleagues. Although this may tend to stack the deck in favor of the man who studied with a renowned scientist and thus suggests the importance of "who you know" as well as "what you know," it would be difficult to argue that this situation diminishes in any way the quality of work that thereby becomes accepted. At worst, it eliminates some, if not much, additional good work from the literature and it does ensure that the coherence of a field's universe of discourse is maintained from one generation to the next through personal ties as well as through the "logic" of the field.

If we assume that the limitations upon the exercise of arbitrary power within science stem from the emphasis upon the equality of all scientists in their right to contribute to knowledge, then, I think we may say that the forces upholding the norm of communality in this final case may be traced again to the conditions that must prevail if the exchange system of science is to continue in operation and scientists are to be assured that they may indeed continue to receive competent response to their work. As was the case with other problems in science, scientists themselves usually support the norms by reference to their functions for the advancement of knowledge—a goal which all of them are assumed to support. But I would argue that it is essentially the desire to maintain a situation in which each scientist may continue to receive in fair share the commodity of competent response that provides the motivation to enforce these norms and to work out structural arrangements whereby they may be optimally implemented.

Summary

In this chapter I have attempted to demonstrate, through an analysis of several "social problems" of science, that the theoretical model of science developed in previous chapters is capable of helping us understand these problems. As I remarked earlier, these analyses cannot show that the model is "true," but I believe that they do allow us to conclude at least that it is "adequate." Certainly there are other aspects of scientists' behavior that might also have been examined, but for reasons of space I have limited myself to those aspects most generally known and most frequently the subject of concern or controversy. For an extremely insightful and more detailed consideration of many more aspects of science, both its problems and various responses to them, the reader is referred to Hagstrom's *The Scientific Community*.

It would perhaps have been desirable to extend this analysis to a comparison of the differences among scientists working in different institutional contexts and in different countries, but data relevant to such comparisons is scarce. Perhaps the best work available now on the former topic is to be found in Krohn (1960, 1961). Kaplan has also done useful work in this area (1965a) as well as in the area of national differences in scientific organization (1962), in which field Meier (1951) and Ben-David (1964) have also made important contributions.

In the concluding chapter, I shall attempt an analysis of how current changes in the scientific community and in its social environment are likely to bring about changes in the social structure and perhaps in the social system of science.

Footnotes for Chapter 6

1. Merton, *Social Theory and Social Structure*, p. 122.
2. Merton, "Resistance to the Systematic Study of Multiple Discoveries in Science," p. 269.
3. Robert K. Merton, "The Ambivalence of Scientists," *Bulletin of the Johns Hopkins Hospital*, vol. 112 (February 1963), p. 81.
4. Robert K. Merton, "Priorities in Scientific Discovery," p. 465.
5. This section is drawn largely from my article, "Basic versus Applied Research: The Conflict Between Means and Ends in Science," *Indian Sociological Bulletin*, vol. 2, no. 1 (October 1964), pp. 34–42; see also my "Research Orientations and Attitudes Toward Teamwork," *IRE Transactions on Engineering Management*, vol. EM-9, 1 (March 1962), pp. 29–33.
6. Bernard Barber, *Science and the Social Order*, p. 99.
7. Harold Wooster, "Letters" column, *Science*, vol. 130, no. 3368, p. 226.
8. William Baumol, "Activity Analysis in One Lesson," *American Economic Review*, December 1958, p. 873; see also: Stewart E. Perry, "Observations

on Social Processes in Psychiatric Research," *Behavioral Science*, vol. 1, no. 4 (October 1956), pp. 296–297.

9. Warren O. Hagstrom, p. 198.

10. Walter Spieth, "Letters" Column, *Science,* vol. 143, no. 3603, p. 197.

11. For a more detailed discussion of the motivational distinctions between scientists with basic and with applied interests and of the social background characteristics that seem related to each, see: Norman W. Storer, *Science and Scientists in an Agricultural Research Organization: A Sociological Study* (unpublished doctoral dissertation, Cornell University, 1961, available through University Microfilms, Inc., Ann Arbor, Michigan, no. 61–6842).

12. Joseph Ben-David, "Roles and Innovations in Medicine," *American Journal of Sociology*, vol. 65, no. 6 (May 1960), p. 557.

13. Ben-David, "Roles and Innovations in Medicine," p. 564.

14. For a more detailed discussion of this problem, see: Bernard Barber, "Resistance by Scientists to Scientific Discovery," pp. 539–556.

15. Alfred de Grazia, ed., *The American Behavioral Scientist*, vol. 7, no. 1 (September 1963), issue on "The Politics of Science and Dr. Velikovsky."

16. Barber, "Resistance by Science to Scientific Discovery," p. 544.

17. Barber, "Resistance by Science to Scientific Discovery," p. 543.

18. F. J. Gruenberger, "A Measure for Crackpots," *Science*, vol. 145, no. 3639, p. 1415.

19. Hagstrom's discussion of secrecy in science, in *The Scientific Community*, pp. 87–99, is particularly instructive; see also the "Letters" column in *Science*, vol. 149, no. 3680, p. 137, and in *Science*, vol. 149, no. 3685, p. 707, for comments concerning the extent to which data presented at scientific meetings should be considered part of the public record.

CHAPTER 7

The Future of the Social System of Science[1]

I pointed out in the preceding chapter that whereas certain problems of science are inherent in the tension between its ideal social system and the realities of the world in which scientists must operate (the compromises between them producing the social structure of science), there are certain other problems that arise whenever changes with which the normative system is not equipped to deal take place in the parameters of that system. It seems to be a general rule that when the environment of an open system (that is, a system that must interact with its environment) changes, there must be related changes in the relations among its parts if it is to continue its corporate existence. Similarly, if there are major changes in the number or in the needs of its component parts, the patterns of interaction among them must change too, to enable them to continue to act interdependently, to participate in the "closed" cycles of interaction that constitute the system's identity, and to meet the new needs.

For instance, the depletion of natural resources in an area (a change in the groups' environment) will force the people in that area to alter their patterns of behavior to some extent, for example, changing from coal mining to the manufacture of furniture or from a hunting economy to a farming economy. If such changes are not made, the groups must either disperse or move away. And if an organization's membership increases greatly in numbers, the old word-of-mouth means of coordinating action may have to be replaced by a newsletter; further, as the number of levels of authority increases, the relationships between leader and followers will change also. Finally, as the "needs" of a group's members change, for instance, from horses to automobiles for transportation—new relationships will develop among them enabling them to satisfy the new need.

The position of science with respect to the larger society has been changing in a way somewhat analogous to these illustrations, and we may expect it to respond to these changes if in fact its members do have a commitment to its continued existence as a distinct social system. Perhaps the most basic change is the increase of society's interest in the products of science and its consequent willingness to support science more generously. This has led in turn to a continuing increase in the size of the scientific community—Derek de Solla Price (1963, pp. 1–32) estimates that its size has been doubling roughly every fifteen years since the early eighteenth century—and to such concommitant phenomena as the "publication explosion" and the increasing interdependence between science and government. Although these things are in actuality inseparable and the scientific community must attempt to cope with them simultaneously, it is impossible to deal analytically with all of them at the same time. Here, then, I must first focus upon them individually, and only thereafter attempt an assessment of the picture as a whole.

I will, therefore, discuss in turn these three major changes in the parameters of the social system of science: the increasing support of science by society, specifically, the relations between science and government; the increasing number of scientists; and the publication explosion. Finally, I shall attempt some broad predictions about the future of science as a social system, trying to take into account the "mix" of problems and of responses to them that will characterize its future.

The Consequences of Increasing Support from Society

"Increasing support" from society refers most specifically to an increase in the amount of money a man may earn by following a career in science and also to an increase in the amount of prestige or respect he receives from other members of society. That such increases have occurred, particularly in the last fifteen years, is supported by a good deal of data on both the incomes and prestige-ranking of scientists; see National Science Foundation (1964) and Hodge, Siegel and Rossi (1964, pp. 286–302). Whether such increases have yet been sufficient to begin to attract a qualitatively different type of person into science cannot be determined; with increasing financial support for graduate work available, it may be simply that a career in science is now open to those who in previous years would have liked to become scientists but who, for some reason or other, could not afford it.

The possibility exists, however, that there will be an increasing number of people seeking admission to graduate departments in the sciences more for the glamour and the practical advantages of a scientific career than from a basic desire to exercise their creative abilities. Most of this group will probably be eliminated along the way by the pressures of graduate work and by their own inability to commit themselves as thoroughly to the work as is necessary. Certainly the efficacy of graduate training as an agency for reshaping people's motivations will be severely tested as science departments will have to train greater numbers of such "undedicated" students. On the whole, though, the likelihood of a substantial increase in the proportion of such people professionally trained does not appear great, and for all practical purposes we may discount the possibility that science will come more and more to be manned by people with career motivations that differ appreciably from those of today's scientists.

A more insidious problem comes with the rise in relative affluence of those who are already scientists or who would have entered science anyway. As the scientist becomes "upwardly mobile" in terms of social class, he will begin to learn new patterns of behavior that will govern his life outside of his laboratory. He will acquire new groups of friends as he moves to a better neighborhood and will probably begin to participate more widely in the life of the community. As life outside of it becomes more rewarding, the laboratory may cease to have such a strong hold on his interests, and the new patterns of behavior and interests developed outside may come into more serious conflict with the norms of science.

Writing in 1954, Lawrence S. Kubie commented on the reverse of this situation:

> What then are some of the economic realities which the young scientist fails to anticipate? First of all, he rarely seems to realize that a day in the laboratory is the same for a rich scientist or a poor one, while the price of poverty will be paid by his family at home. He does not accept the full import of the fact that his wife and his youngsters are the ones who will have to spend 24 hours a day in quarters so crowded that they will lack space for peaceful family living and the dignity of privacy.[2]

Today it seems much less likely that the laboratory will seem so markedly preferable to the home and the neighborhood and its special attraction from this standpoint is probably diminishing somewhat. The lure of laboratory life, where behavior is more naturally guided by the norms of science, is thus meeting greater competition from the "good life" at home in the better suburbs where different norms apply. As one's activities away from the laboratory become increasingly attractive, the attitudes and interests appropriate to them come to be more important to the scientist; he may as a result experience greater conflict within himself over his goals and interests as the demands of the two different styles of life upon him come to acquire equal strength.

This is certainly not to argue that scientists *should* be poor, for they are human beings as well as scientists, but simply to point out that, from this point of view and other things being equal, the relative poverty in which scientists used to live was probably good for *science*. It meant that a greater proportion of the scientist's satisfactions in life were to be found in the laboratory and thus presumably produced a stronger commitment to the social system of science. Nor is this to argue that a devaluation of "life in science" is a necessary consequence of the scientist's rise in affluence, although the changing situation seems to make this more likely than an actual increase in commitment to science.

The values of the larger society, its greater interest in money, prestige, and perhaps in power or influence, may come also to play a larger part in the relations among scientists. When scientists begin to feel that their colleagues are more interested in these commodities, if only because such interests have become a more important part of their lives away from the laboratory, the commodity of competent response to creativity will be challenged by the commodities that are more negotiable outside the laboratory. A scientist's reputation may come to rest as much upon the amount of time he spends traveling about the country to meetings and as a consultant as upon the quality of his publications; it may be shaped more by the size of the research project he is administering than by the influence his work has upon the work of others. It seems possible, in other words, that the autonomy of the exchange-system of science may be weakened simply because scientists come to assume that their colleagues no longer value competent response so much more highly than other commodities. Subtle pressures to violate the norm of disinterestedness may thus increase, even though the norm itself will continue to be defended, perhaps even by the denial that the possibilities outlined above are at all likely.

It is a basic fact that when society supports an activity, it expects something in return. The vast bulk of federal research support goes to "research and development" rather than to basic research, and, as was pointed out in the previous chapter, even the support of basic research is largely a consequence of the expectation that sooner or later it will prove to have practical application. When the federal government supports research, it must be able to give a satisfactory accounting to the voters of what it expects to receive in return for this expenditure of tax money. Similarly, a corporation must be able to persuade its stockholders that their money is being wisely (that is, profitably) invested in research. To be sure, the practice of describing a proposed program of basic research so as to emphasize its potentially practical results has been a major device for giving both the scientist and the granting agency what they want, and it may be that eventually the taxpayer and the stockholder will come to define the expenditure of a given amount of research funds for basic research as comparable to the accepted practice now of paying employees for the time they spend on their coffee break: that is, because it is necessary for the continued efficiency of the entire operation.

One unfortunate aspect of this situation now, however, is the tendency to glorify as "basic" much research that is actually directed toward the solution of immediate, practical problems. Just as the scientist may describe his essentially "basic" work as "applied" in order to obtain support for it, so the scientist who is engaged in applied research or the company seeking to hire scientists for such work may be tempted to define it as "basic" in order to enhance its appeal to the scientific community. Although this confusion of terms will not directly affect the quality of research carried out, it may leave the scientist confused as to the nature of his audience; it may also produce misleading titles, making more difficult the problem of identifying the substantive contents of articles and technical reports by their titles alone, that is, in references and bibliographies. Because people may well be generally more intelligent about what they are doing than the sociologist tends to give them credit for, it seems unlikely to me that this situation will become a serious problem; however, as one of many small but growing problems, it may contribute to a cumulating pressure upon the present-day structure of science and lead to marked changes in it.

The relations between science and government are a very important subject for the analysis of increasing social support for science. Although the enhanced prestige that the scientist commands today cannot be controlled directly by the government, certainly a good deal of the credit for his rising income may be traced directly or indirectly to this source. Probably the greatest incentive to industry to invest more in research has been the government's interest in atomic energy and space, as well as the increasing technical sophistication of defense systems in general.

The increased demand for scientists on the part of both government and industry, together with the sharp rise in college enrollments, has created a market situation in which the seller, the scientist, is able to command a higher price for his services, research and teaching. The role of the federal government has thus been crucial in enlarging society's support for science, and recognition of the problems involved in this relationship has given rise to a large body of literature concerned with the reciprocal influences between science and government. (See Dupre and Lakoff, 1962, Gilpin and Wright, 1964, and Price, 1954, 1965.)

This is not the place to go deeply into this work, but it is important to note here that the increased dependence of science upon government for its support has led to certain structural changes within science. This has meant primarily the development of a cadre of scientists to advise the government on both policy decisions and on the allocation of research funds and for whom service in this capacity has come to represent a new type of professional recognition. To be sure, excellence in scientific achievement is generally a prerequisite for such activities, but to the extent that the opportunity to advise the government becomes a major source of gratification for scientists and a major symbol of recognition, excellence in research may come more definitely to be seen as a means rather than as an end. Moreover, inasmuch as many first-rate scientists have no interest in such activities, or lack the personal skills necessary to undertake them successfully, participation in this sort of work cannot be an index always of scientific achievement. It is instead the "reward" for possessing a combination of skills, some of them unrelated to scientific excellence, and the intrinsic importance of professional recognition as affirmative response to creativity may come to be watered down. As the younger scientist sees that "worldly" success is possible and that it involves more than scientific creativity, he may be persuaded that competent response is less valuable to other scientists, if not to him, and he may thus alter accordingly his standards for evaluating their behavior.

If there is not a high degree of mutual faith among scientists that all are seeking competent response to creativity rather than money, prestige, and influence, then their motivation to support the norms of science, which as I have pointed out are simultaneously functional for the advancement of knowledge and for the adequate allocation of competent response, will weaken. In this sense, the norm of disinterestedness is absolutely vital to the protection of the autonomy of science, and if it fails as a defense, the entire system that produces advances in certified knowledge may crumble. This too, however, is an extremely remote probability. By ignoring all of the countervailing pressures that serve to protect science, one may easily produce such gloom-and-doom predictions in abundance.

One of these countervailing pressures may lie in the fact that heavy government support for research is apparently weakening the scientist's ties to his local university. The government rather than the university has become his "patron," and frequently he is able to move from one university to another with his research funds intact. Other things being equal, this would certainly seem to promote a more cosmopolitan orientation in the scientist, for his attention would thus be focused more directly upon his discipline than upon the specific organization in which he happens to work. Regardless of the threat that this situation poses to the cohesiveness of the university, a problem that has caused some genuine concern to university administrators, it probably does have some positive consequences for the social system of science.

My point, however, is that the general threat to the norm of disinterestedness posed by society's increased support of science is indeed another threat to the autonomy of science; no matter how minor it is, I believe that it is adding in some way to the pressures that are now impinging upon science and may eventually bring about a marked change in its social organization.

The Consequences of Increasing Growth of the Scientific Community

As I pointed out at the beginning of this chapter, a marked increase in the number of members of an organization must result in the establishment of different patterns of communication among them and different techniques for coordinating their activities if the organization is to retain its identity. This is, of course, particularly true when their actions must be fairly tightly coordinated, but it is true even in the case of more amorphous groups whose members' interactions are entirely voluntary rather than controlled by a central authority in the service of a single, well-defined goal. If, as Derek Price (1963) suggests, the population of the scientific community is doubling every fifteen years or so and roughly 90 percent of all scientists who have ever lived are alive today, then certain structural consequences should already be quite visible, and more should be in the offing as this population continues to grow.

A group generally has two major responses open to it under such circumstances. Further differentiation accompanied by more effective means of integration is the first, whereas splitting to form two or more separate groups, each small enough to be manageable under the old pattern of organization, is the second. We cannot say that such responses are orderly, or even that there is a clear sense of direction on the part of the participants as they try to adapt to the challenge of increased size, but only that eventually one or the other type of response will be forthcoming in relatively clear form. As a company grows in size, for instance, jobs formerly done by the same individual will be assigned to different individuals, and as that company continues growing, these tasks may be handled by departments rather than by particular individuals. The coordination of their actions is guided by those in control of the company's financial resources and carried out through its system of internal communications. It is only when the company reaches really giant size that integration becomes a major problem; the usual problem is to seek increased efficiency in these communications, but it may also happen that some divisions split off to become financially independent of the parent organization (with the original company management's consent) and that some are sold. The same general phenomenon is to be found in non-economic systems, too.

In a social system whose continued existence does not depend upon the tight coordination of all participants' actions and where the adequate allocation of the motivating rewards is not the responsibility of a centralized body, the point at which the process of differentiation proceeds beyond the system's ability to keep all its parts integrated is difficult to identify. Frequently the "logic" of specialization will be followed without regard for the capacity of the system's integrative mechanisms, so that various parts find themselves so specialized that they have no clear-cut patterns of behavior through which to relate themselves to other parts. At this point the "splitting-off" response to growth has occurred, whether or not it was intended by the members of the system.

The integration of the social system of science is based primarily upon the existence of relatively clear-cut "channels of implication," that is, channels of relevance and communication through which the implications of one body of work for another are indicated. It is the office of theory to point out these channels of implication, and as such, theory is vitally important as a means for integrating the scientific community. Yet theory not only organizes and integrates research findings, but also opens up new questions and new areas for study. These questions, plus the discovery that new empirical findings cannot be accounted for by existing theory, mean that the principal integrative mechanism of science is continually being strained; there is a constant race between theory and research both to predict new findings in advance and to find data that will bring about modifications in theory.

When we add to this contest an increasing number of men who are engaged both in theory-building and in research, the problem is further complicated. Not only must the theory "fit" the new findings but it must also be communicated widely so that scientists' activities can be oriented to the same advancing frontier of certified knowledge. One aspect of this problem is characterized by the term "publication explosion," and that will, therefore, be treated in the next section of this chapter, but more broadly it raises the question of whether the activities of an ever greater number of individuals can continue to be coordinated indefinitely.

The history of science seems to show that it is when theoretical structure is lacking, the previous structure having been overthrown and its successor not yet established, that there is the greatest degree of social disorganization within science. Kuhn's discussion (1962) of science during "revolutionary" and "normal" times suggests this, and presumably other data could be marshalled to test this hypothesis more thoroughly. The point is that when there is relatively little guidance for scientists by which to determine what problems will seem important to their colleagues or to assess the importance of others' findings, there will be a great weakening of the bonds that serve to integrate the scientific community—that is, a weakening of the feeling on the part of all participants that there exist common standards for the judgment of creativity and that competent response to creativity can be fairly obtained. It is at such times that the tendency toward scientific fraud is strongest, as is also the tendency to separate into distinct "schools" in acrimonious battle with one another.

We may guess, then, that at least indirectly the growth in the number of working scientists will begin to place greater strain upon the integrative capabilities of theory as these scientists turn out more and more research findings. Not only is a greater volume of data being produced each year, but it seems likely that as a field increases in membership, there is a decrease in the proportion of its members whose concern is principally with theory; this may be accounted for by the fact that a greater proportion of new recruits are less capable of working at the level of comprehensive theory, although it is also likely that competition among theorists may be more pronounced because there is so little "room at the top" and that fewer survive the competition. If it is true that the more scientists there are, the fewer will be involved in theory, and this is by no means proven, the chances are that theory, which provides channels of implication among different fields and which thereby serves more to integrate science as a whole, not only one or another of its separate subfields, will slowly begin to fail in meeting the vital responsibility of integration.

If this were to come about, it might follow that the major subdivisions of science would become more and more independent of one another until the concept of a single, intellectually integrated community of science were no more than a reference to a past golden age. How *likely* this is to occur, however, is another matter; it is at least, if not more likely, that scientists will again come up with something new, such as the increasingly promising General Systems Theory, that will provide a new basis for the integration of the entire scientific community. At minimum, the existence of predictions in this vein argue the need for new forms of theory, the search for higher levels of generalization, and the encouragement of generalists who are able to facilitate communication among different branches of scientific endeavor.

Interdisciplinary groups of all sorts also contribute a good deal to the maintenance of at least the impression of a pan-scientific integration, although in only a few cases have they as yet supported this impression by the establishment of detailed channels of implication that span the entire spectrum of scientific interests. The popularity of interdisciplinary research seems to wax and wane over time, and one might conclude that such efforts merely represent a recurring fad. But after each peak of interest in such research, it seems likely that even as the groups take up their separate ways again they bring back with them the seeds of closer integration with each other. So long as a basic goal of science is to produce generalized knowledge, we may expect that attempts to integrate the different fields of scientific knowledge will continue and come gradually closer to success as time passes.

Of course integrative mechanisms also exist that do not depend on scientific theory but on other interests that scientists hold in common. The most important of these is the national organization of scientists *per se*, which in this country is the American Association for the Advancement of Science. Although this still serves primarily as an important channel for the communication of research findings through its weekly journal, *Science*, it is apparently coming more and more to serve also as a representative of the scientific community to society at large. *Science* now has an American circulation of over 100,000 and seems to be becoming increasingly important as a kind of "house organ" for scientists. A report of a recent survey of AAAS members' attitudes toward material appearing in *Science* (based on the responses of 2542 readers, 58 percent of the number sampled)[3] shows that whereas 40 percent of the readers would like to see more research reports, almost as many (35 percent) would like more "News and Comment." Forty-five percent of the respondents ranked the journal's articles as being of most interest to them, whereas the second largest single group, 20 percent, indicated that the "News and Comment" section was most interesting. Slightly less than this proportion of the readers were most interested in the research reports themselves. It seems fairly obvious, then, that membership in the AAAS is motivated by a concern for the profession as a whole rather than by one's particular research interests and that the organization may thus be of increasing importance in the integration of the scientific community.

Another sort of organization is the American Association of University Professors, a group that may represent scientists', as well as other academicians', interests at least vis-à-vis the universities, although it has no specific concern with science and is thus much less important in the integration of the scientific community as a whole. Other large groups such as the American Federation of Societies for Experimental Biology act generally as "holding companies" for their member groups, sponsoring large meetings and publishing many journals so as to take responsibility for these matters off the shoulders of the smaller groups. Such organizations as the Federation may also assume responsibility for maintaining relations with other fields of science, inasmuch as its member groups may already be assumed to share common interests with specialties in other fields.

There is another aspect of the growth of science as well, one that does not directly involve scientists in their capacity as researchers but simply as participants in a social system. Just as in other human groups, an increase in the number of members will lead to increasing vertical differentiation, the distinction between the "leaders" and the "led" or between the elite and the rank and file is becoming more visible. Ranking of this sort within science now is based primarily on scientific achievement, with the prestige of one's local institution being but one, partially independent, measure of one's "social class" within science. But as the scientific community grows, it is likely that there will be more "stratification" within it and less effective communication between different strata. There may also be more attention paid to problems of "social mobility" and to the different "life styles" that characterize different strata.

It is by no means proven, for instance, that the "best" men are always hired by the top ten or twenty universities in the country or by a select group of industries and government agencies, although the representation of these institutions on government panels and in the leadership of professional societies would certainly suggest this. It may be that the young scientist who is hired by one of these institutions is somehow encouraged to do better work than he might have done at a second- or third-rate institution, so that the institution makes the man rather than vice versa. Or it may be that his affiliation will give him more direct access to the important men in his field so that he has an edge in gaining access to journals and in receiving greater opportunity to demonstrate his abilities. In any case, to the extent that a person's social class within science depends upon where he received his graduate education or held his first position, we may say that there is indeed a type of stratification within science that is based upon more than scientific achievement alone. Data tending to support these speculations are to be found in a recent paper by Crane (1965).

As the population of the scientific community increases, this situation is likely to become more obvious, even though ladders of "upward mobility" for the genuinely talented may become more readily available also. Given the ever-present sense of competition within science, and the general tendency of the unsuccessful to blame their failure on something besides their own lack of merit, it may be that the unsuccessful will come increasingly to feel that their failures are due to the structure of the community itself rather than to their own performance, due to unfair advantages that others have gained only by virtue of their positions in the social-class structure of science. If the symbols of stratification become more obvious, as it is likely they will, such complaints will seem more legitimate and may presage a real failure of the motivational system that underlies the social system. To the extent that the ability to be creative depends more and more upon access to expensive equipment as well as to the attention of one's colleagues, a belief in the existence of "irrelevant" factors that play a role in the distribution of such equipment and attention and thereby interfere with one's opportunity to participate in the exchange-system might well undermine one's commitment to scientific activity itself. This would mean disillusion with the rules of the game rather than with one's skill in playing it, and it would lead either to more scientists quitting it altogether or to an increasing tension and hostility among scientists which would seriously weaken the mutual trust so necessary to keep the exchange system operating adequately.

Growth simply in number of members, then, seems likely to lead to a number of potentially dysfunctional consequences for science. To be sure, the scientific community has been growing fairly steadily over the past three centuries and has been able thus far to adjust to changes resulting from this growth, but this does not necessarily mean that it will continue to be so successful in the future. I have pointed out in this section several problems that attend continued growth and might have serious consequences for the social system of science in the future; although it is extremely difficult to be certain of the magnitude of these problems (because it is difficult to estimate the strength of the forces which will be forthcoming to resolve them), it seems likely that the maintenance of the social system of science in its present state will become more and more problematic. Whether it can continue successfully to produce advances in certified knowledge under a radically different form of organization seems problematic as well, although because so little is really known now, it is impossible to be entirely pessimistic about the matter.

The Consequences of the "Publication Explosion"[4]

    In order to discuss the possible effects of the continuous increase in the rate of publication of scientific information, it is necessary first to develop a clear understanding of the symbolic importance of the idea of "the literature" in the social system of science. The term refers in one sense to the physical existence of the books and journals that together contain all the reports of research and ideas that scientists have produced, but it has two usually unspoken implications that are of more direct concern to us here. The first of these has been discussed earlier: the fact that a research report has been "made public" through the distribution of multiple copies seems to give it a kind of existence independent of the knowledge possessed by any particular individual or group of individuals; it becomes a part of the universal body of knowledge to which scientists refer in their work. The second implication is that something "in" the literature is enduringly available for public inspection; scientists are somehow expected to have access to knowledge that exists "out there" in the literature, even though they are not assumed to be able to know something that exists only in the heads or personal files of a few individuals. In theory, this may be the converse of the first; in practice, the implementation of this expectation is crucial in supporting the ability of scientists to accept the independent reality of this knowledge.

    Communication between scientists must be based upon the assumption that both parties hold a considerable amount of knowledge in common so that they need not start from scratch on every occasion. And the fact that they most frequently communicate about the extension of knowledge means particularly that they must be acquainted with the most recent additions to the established body of knowledge; this in turn means that a very important criterion of being a working scientist is that one have reasonably easy access to the literature so that he may stay abreast of it. Without a general faith on the part of all scientists that their colleagues are in fact able to do this, their assumption that they will be able to obtain competent response to their creativity (that is, to their attempts add to the current state of knowledge) will be weakened. Without being able to know specifically just what other scientists actually know at any given moment, one must assume at least that they *want* to keep up with new developments and that they are realistically capable of doing this.

In this sense, the continued existence of the social system of science depends upon there being evidence continuously available that one's colleagues are indeed able collectively to keep abreast of new knowledge as it is added to the literature. And even without their implementing this responsibility perfectly, each accepts the obligation to "keep up"; it is as much the admission of this responsibility as the actual meeting of it that is important in maintaining scientists' collective trust that they are indeed working within a common universe of discourse.

An important foundation of part of this trust must be both a shared definition of what constitutes "the literature" and specific mechanisms (libraries and journals) that make it available to all. This definition of "the literature," however, is by no means clear-cut. Certain channels of printed communication are clearly within the boundaries of the literature, for example, major professional journals and monograph series, and books whose titles clearly indicate their relevance to scientific topics; there are many more channels that are definitely outside these boundaries; and there is a number of others that seem to straddle the boundaries.

A case in point is the recent controversy over a policy announced in the January 1, 1960, issue of *Physical Review Letters*, an "express journal," published weekly by the American Institute of Physics so that important findings of general interest to physicists may be disseminated in brief form with maximum speed. Because of its speed in reporting new findings, it has come also to serve as a means for establishing priority, even though this function is considered irrelevant to its purposes and even undesirable by its editor. The editor announced that, "Scientific discoveries are not the proper subject for newspaper scoops. . . . In the future, we may reject papers whose main contents have been published previously in the daily press."[5] On November 1, 1962, the *Applied Physics Letters* announced in a similar vein, "Work described elsewhere, for example, in press releases or in the form of abstracts of contributed papers, prior to scheduled publication in *APL*, will not be considered eligible for publication."[6]

The editor of *Science*, noting that he had been asked by the American Institute of Physics to adhere to their position, objected that newspaper reporters and editors, despite the excellence of some science reporters, cannot be expected to give full or entirely accurate accounts of scientists' findings, and that this was, therefore, an undesirable policy. He agreed that "It is tempting to try to reform operators [that is, those who seek public esteem and priority through giving out press releases] by denying them publication in scientific journals" but suggested that responsibility for this really rests at the local level, "with the man's scientific colleagues, with his superiors, and with properly constituted news bureaus."[7]

Neither party faced the central issue, that of whether science reporting and features in the daily newspapers, even the most respected of them, should fairly be considered part of the standard literature of the field. Certainly the question would never have arisen if the only newspaper in question had been the Podunk *Weekly Clarion*, but because the top American newspapers are received by major libraries the world over, it might have been reasonable to assume that physicists actually have access to them as readily as they do to the *Physical Review Letters* and the *Applied Physics Letters*. But because reading such newspapers regularly is not part of their expected behavior as scientists, as well as because newspaper editors are not technically competent to assess the goodness of research reported by their own personnel, I think that Abelson was correct in protesting the announced policy. Such a policy would in effect grant legitimacy as part of the literature of physics to such newspapers as *The New York Times* and the *Washington Post*, not to speak of all other newspapers that use the major wire services, and would effectively do away with the right of physicists to monitor and control the materials that are added to the body of established knowledge in their field. At minimum, then, the boundaries of the literature must include only those channels of communication to which most scientists in a field are regularly exposed and which are able to guarantee the soundness of the materials they carry.

The problem of publication in obscure journals—publications that are definitely concerned with a particular field of science but may have relatively limited circulation and be known as uncritical in their acceptance of materials—is related to this issue, as is the problem of publication in foreign journals. The traditional requirement of competence in one or two languages (generally French and German, at least until the recent emergence of Russian as a major language of science) as prerequisite to earning the doctorate is intended to ensure that a scholar may be legitimately held responsible for knowing the literature of his field without regard for the particular languages in which it appears. Although this principle is still kept alive, the actual percentage of American scientists who account themselves reasonably competent in one or more foreign languages is rather small; only the increasing tendency for English to become the standard language of world science has enabled American scientists to avoid serious difficulties because of their linguistic weaknesses.

That the principle of complete responsibility for "knowing the literature" is still expected to be in force is illustrated by a remark of Pitirim A. Sorokin in his *Fads and Foibles in Modern Sociology*. In one passage he footnotes the observation: "Though these studies repeat and confirm the results of many previous studies" in this way:

> Among these studies, my study on the "Influence of Occupation Upon Behavior and Psychological Processes" ("Vliianie professii no provedenie ludei"), *Journal Psichologii i Nevrologii*, No. 1, 1921, pp. 397–424, showed. . . .[8]

It is extremely unlikely that this article would have been available in Russian, much less in translation, to the authors of "these [American] studies," yet Sorokin seems implicitly to be claiming some measure of priority in this area by virtue of a publication some 25 years earlier in what was then to Americans a relatively obscure language. It is at points like this that the principle of responsibility for knowing the literature, and the empirical possibility that scientists can in fact live up to this responsibility, seem to clash.

Today, we are more concerned with the other end of the stick, not the *in*accessibility of parts of the literature but the fact that too much *is* accessible. The scientist today is so inundated by the contributions of his colleagues that time is simply not available for him to keep abreast of all of them. This problem was discussed briefly in the preceding chapter with reference to violations of the norm of organized scepticism, but the implications of such problems for the future social organization of science have yet to be discussed fully.

Perhaps the most important implication is the possibility of a change in the basic assumptions that until now have seemed to underlie scientists' use of the term, "the literature," in such phrases as "a search through the literature reveals" or "the literature contains few references to X." When the flood of new information becomes so great that it becomes increasingly unreasonable for scientists to expect one another to be able to stay in full command of it, the older assumption that publication in one of the legitimate journals was sufficient to assure a contribution's permanent place in the literature will come to be replaced by the assumption that publication is no more than communication with a *particular* audience. Once this is accepted, both the ideal of an absolute baseline against which creativity is to be measured and the scientist's sense that he is contributing to a universally recognized fund of knowledge will be weakened.

Among other things, such a change in basic assumptions may lead to a greater amount of redundancy in the literature as scientists become more willing to publish essentially the same material in two or more journals that seem to have distinctly different audiences. To the extent that this occurs more frequently, the publication explosion will proceed at an even faster rate.

We have no knowledge of whether the increased amount of publications has produced a substantial increase in the average amount of time required for a scientist to become aware of a book or article relevant to his own work. Possibly it has not, although certainly it cannot have reduced this period of time. The scientific grapevine and the abstracting services will eventually announce an article's existence to all who are interested in it, but if the lag between an article's appearance and awareness of it increases appreciably, certain difficulties will ensue. In the utilitarian sense, there will be a greater amount of wasted effort due to duplication, and when it becomes harder for a scientist to appreciate another's priority (because he may suspect that someone else, as yet unknown to him, has published the same findings earlier), the rate of circulation of competent response within science will slow down.

When the ability to recognize priority is weakened because the literature is too vast for any scientist to keep abreast of it, the keystone of the social system will be weakened. If the concept of "absolute priority" is lost, just as the concept of "absolute simultaneity" has been lost to the physical sciences since Einstein's work on Relativity, a partial state of anomie may result because the conditions under which creativity has meaning will have changed.

We might suppose that a good deal of the concern expressed by scientists about the publication explosion has its roots in their fear that competent response to their own work will be more difficult to obtain, even though hesitance to proclaim their interest in professional recognition makes them formulate their arguments in terms of a fear of inefficiency and wasteful duplication of effort. This concern has generated a good deal of interest in the development of new mechanisms that would offset the difficulties of keeping up with the literature by making access to it quicker and more efficient. Most of these efforts have concentrated upon the problem of information retrieval, generally with some form of automation seen as the most effective way to accomplish this. Many people have pointed out that a system of distributing information entirely on the basis of demand will be qualitatively different from the current one in which much information is presented to individuals without its having been specifically requested (see Back, 1962). A "demand" system, in essence, is like a library, where the individual ordinarily must know ahead of time what it is that he wants; subscription to a journal, on the other hand, makes one part of a "guaranteed audience" so that one automatically receives whatever is carried by this channel of communication. The latter is certainly more effective in enabling the contributor to feel that he is living up to the norm of communality and also carries the implicit assurance that his contribution is indeed widely available to his colleagues.

Yet the sheer volume of scientific publication today has made it appear to many that a "demand" system is the only reasonable solution to the problem of how to get the greatest amount of useful information to scientists without seriously overloading their scanning capacities. This plan, however, has not met with much enthusiasm from the scientific community. Alvin Weinberg, chairman of the panel that prepared the report on "Science, Government, and Information" for the President's Science Advisory Council, notes:

> In spite of these advantages [of a centralized depository, from which copies of contributions can be distributed upon request after being announced by title lists and abstract bulletins], the technical community has always rejected the central depository, largely, I believe, because scientists are reluctant to give up the prestige that attaches to publication in a technical journal.[9]

I suggest that scientists' reluctance to give up this "prestige" is based upon something more than pure egotism or the publish-or-perish philosophy. The fact of publication, as it has traditionally been defined (that is, publication in a journal that reaches a guaranteed audience) means that one's work is immediately available to all of those who subscribe to the journal, usually the scientists who are most likely to be interested in the topic and most competent to respond to it. There is always the chance that these scientists might not notice the listing of the contribution in a title-list or an abstract bulletin, or that they might not order it even if they did. It is only when an article is clearly and directly relevant to a scientist's work that he will take special pains to obtain it; if it is not so obviously important to him, the fact that it is not immediately available to him may lead him to ignore it altogether. It is thus the assumption, supported only by publication in a journal, that one's work will be immediately available to one's colleagues that makes this form of scientific communication more appropriate to the social system of science, and therefore more "prestigious" than any contribution that is simply filed in a central depository to await specific requests for it.

A more appropriate response to the publication explosion is to be seen in the growing tendency of professional scientific societies to publish a review journal that is received by all members, as well as a number of more specialized journals that are received by those members particularly interested in their contents. Although this may not be as efficient as information-retrieval in making this information readily and widely accessible, it does allow a man both to publish his work in archival form—in a regular journal—and, at the same time, to announce its existence to a much wider, guaranteed audience. In other words, it allows the scientist to live up to some of the norms of science—particularly the norm of communality—more fully than any other system now known.

Enhancing the importance of the review journal, however, does not seem likely to solve the problem entirely, and as the publication explosion grows, the problem may come to be that there are too many review journals for a scientist to cover adequately. Nor will more sophisticated retrieval systems solve it, for they can by definition only be useful in response to specific requests; with information retrieval systems that cross-reference contributions by subject-matter, the requestor may be faced with too many articles to read, and it is possible that even here the production of new materials may exceed the ability of the retrieval-system to keep up with them.

A more radical and increasingly important response to the problem, which seems to be becoming more and more important, is essentially that of reverting to systems of informal communication among small groups of scientists who know each other and are working on the same problem. Derek Price (1963, pp. 62–91) was the first to point out the existence and growing importance of such groups, calling them invisible colleges and comparing them with the informal group at "Gresham College" that led to the founding of the Royal Society in the mid-seventeenth century. The members of these groups communicate by means of the exchange of reprints and technical reports, through attendance at meetings where they can get together to exchange ideas and information, and by visiting one another's laboratories. Publication in the formal sense comes, under these circumstances, to be "for the record" rather than for purposes of immediate communication; the use of the term, "archival publication,"[10] seems a sign that this explicit purpose of formal publication is coming to be accepted.

The growing importance of such informal groups within science, groups that depend more upon their own private communications system than upon "the literature" itself, is likely to have major implications for the future of science. A discussion of these implications as well as of the implications of the other major changes in the scientific community, which have been noted above, will form the basis of the concluding section.

The Future State of the Scientific Community

There is a natural tendency for anyone who would predict the future to take his knowledge of the present, imperfect as it may be, as his baseline and to measure change against that, even when in fact many of the things he is predicting are already half-way to fruition at the time he is predicting their future appearance. This is particularly likely to be the case here, for we have so little knowledge about the present state of the scientific community; it may well be that some will think I am only predicting what is already here, so far as they are concerned. Even having a tentative model of the phenomenon under consideration will not necessarily be helpful, for specification of the important variables involved is not the same thing as knowing the relative weights each will have in determining the future state of the phenomenon. But for the sake of provoking thought and argument, as well as further research, I think it is worthwhile to indicate what seem to me the most likely changes the scientific community will experience in the next 25 to 35 years.

Underlying these predictions, such as they may be, are my assumptions that society will continue to support science handsomely and that both the number of scientists and the rate of scientific publication will continue to increase. These trends will produce a number of "pressures" upon the social structure of science, many of which will seem to be pushing it in the same general direction whereas a few may begin to push it in an opposite direction; out of this conflux of different forces will emerge the major characteristics of the scientific community in the near future.

First of all, due principally to society's generous support of science, there will come a gradual elevation of the importance of applied research. This is already apparent in efforts to emphasize the practical "spin off" expected to come from basic research, particularly the current efforts that the National Aeronautics and Space Administration is making in connection with its space program. And because men are likely to honor what they think their fellows honor as much as they are to be guided solely by their own values, I think that sooner or later scientists will come to feel that since their colleagues apparently respect applied achievement more than formerly, they will come to define it as just as praiseworthy and important as basic research. It was apparently much easier to defend the sanctity of basic research in the days before World War II, when very little of it was supported directly by government funds, and thus to maintain its invidious superiority over applied research. But with the greater need now to defend the importance of basic research so that it may continue to receive its present high level of government support and with this defense based usually on the promise of eventual practical benefits, I do not think that we can expect applied research to occupy the "underdog" position much longer even in terms of values; certainly in terms of volume of support, it has always been far ahead of basic research.

Particularly since the expectation of achievement in practical matters gives the scientist higher standing in society and more opportunity to be influential in local and national affairs, this trend will be encouraged by the increasing interest of scientists in commodities such as prestige and influence that circulate in the larger society and that scientists have recently become accustomed to enjoy in greater measure than ever before. And when there are so many scientists that each one recognizes how small his chances to achieve a prominent position within "pure" science have become, there may be greater readiness to turn to applied work where the criteria of success are more visible and more easily appreciated by laymen as well as colleagues.

This trend will, I think, add more impetus to the tendency to organize the scientific community on the basis of its members' common career-interests rather than through the integration of the general body of knowledge with which they are all assumed to be concerned. This will mean the development of a sharper distinction between research-specialty groups and career-interest groups, with the latter being by far the larger and more influential within the community as a whole. This trend seems to be fairly well along at the present time, particularly in the physical sciences, yet full recognition of the situation and the concommitant adjustments in the normative structure of science are still to come.

Already the feeling is growing on the part of some academic scientists that the larger of their professional societies are coming to serve a different sort of audience. An indication of this is found in Strauss and Rainwater's *The Professional Scientist*:

> . . . an associate professor of physiological chemistry, who finds the American Society of Biological Chemists more important than the American Chemical Society, remarks: "Sometimes I wonder why in the hell I belong to the ACS. I guess I like their professional journals. I guess my biggest bone of contention is the *News* which is always shouting about who and what. I'm interested in knowing if there is a new advance in biochemistry. I want good articles, not advertising, not personal relations."[11]

The audience of these major scientific organizations will continue to change as they become larger—perhaps mainly because they publish the major journals in the field (those having the widest circulation) and make these available to members at a discount—and as they include more and more scientists outside of academia. These members' interests in reports of applied research, as well as in "news" sections on "who and what," will have an influence on the contents of these journals, with the result that feelings of alienation among academic scientists may increase.

Another sign of increasing professionalization is to be seen in the increasing number of attempts to construct a general "code of ethics" that would govern scientists' relations with the government, with suppliers of scientific instruments, with employers, with their research subjects in the case of the social sciences, and with their colleagues. That such efforts have been met mostly by a great deal of apathy, and sometimes by open rejection as well, seems to indicate that any substantial development of a "we-professionals" feeling within science is still some time away in the future. Yet I believe that this feeling will develop more clearly and more strongly well before the end of the century.

The consequence will be that basic scientists will probably take less and less interest in the organizational affairs of the major societies and will instead devote themselves to the smaller, specialty-oriented groups and to their "invisible colleges," so that the large organizations will come more and more to represent career-interests rather than intellectual interests. And without the major societies and journals to represent so strongly the scientific community's integration on the basis of its members' concern with building an organized body of knowledge, the community will certainly become more differentiated if not simply dissolved into a congeries of unrelated parts.

The emergence of invisible colleges as the centers of advanced basic research in most fields of science will in some respects further these trends. Developing in response to the increasing delays involved in achieving archival publication, which is due in turn to the publication explosion itself, such groups of men who announce and discuss their work mainly through informal communication networks will be less concerned with the "public" nature and concerns of the larger scientific community, and will presumably offer less resistance to such trends. Basic research in general may come to be more sharply separated from the interests of the major professional groups and will instead become a kind of suburb of the scientific metropolis, a suburb comprising the universities where those who have a deep interest in and capacity for advanced basic research will concentrate their energies.

Further, because membership in these informal groups may become more and more dependent upon where one received his graduate training and whom one knows personally, the existence of these groups through adding a degree of rigidity to the stratification system within science, may actually limit to a smaller proportion of scientists the genuine opportunity to participate in basic research on the "hotter" frontiers of science. Their existence may thus force a greater proportion of scientists to turn their interests to applied research and to the affairs of the larger professional scientific organizations. This prediction receives some support in Glaser's (1964, pp. 108–109) work on medical scientists. He found that when the prospect of their organization's shifting toward a substantial emphasis on applied as well as basic research was suggested, roughly 20 percent more of those scientists with "low recognition" (which we may interpret here as the sense of being unable for some reason to achieve satisfactory participation in the social system of basic research) than with "high recognition" were more pleased and less worried by the shift to applied research.

But because scientists will continue to receive their training in the universities, where at least some members of nearly every department will be involved in invisible colleges and will have some influence upon their students' attitudes, it does not seem possible simply to suggest that the members of these groups will cease to be influential in the affairs of the larger community. So long as the major organizations continue to profess a central concern with the advancement of knowledge, these men will be honored; it may be that they will be treated rather more as saints—as being *so* good that it is unrealistic to expect everyone to be like them—than as working colleagues of most scientists, but they will continue to occupy honorific positions within the organizations.

This situation will produce increasing conflict within the role of the academic scientist. He will be drawn on the one hand to the "outside," to the affairs of the larger community and its giant organizations, and on the other hand to his own research interests and the small group of men with whom he is in intensive communication concerning his work. In response to these conflicts we may expect to find an increasing tendency for the scientist to compartmentalize his different activities so that he may engage in each of them without too much confusion. The practice of allowing a scientist one or two days a week for consulting and "professional" activities away from the campus is already becoming established in some universities. Another response may be to recognize more explicitly the major turning point a man faces midway in his career, the problem of whether to stay in the laboratory and forego more intensive participation in professional affairs or to become more involved in research administration and then in a kind of "scientific statesmanship" in his professional organizations.

I do not think that the proposal to make a sharper distinction between responsibilities for teaching and for research—or perhaps between teaching and professional activities of any sort—will be successful in restructuring the role of the academic scientist. To the extent that a scientist needs an audience for his thinking, he has a particularly reliable set of listeners in his students, and I do not think it likely that scientists in general will be willing to give up the pleasure of introducing students to their subjects or of training graduate students to become participants in the social system of science. Regardless of which direction a man's career in science takes, his interest in being responsible for some teaching is not likely to diminish.

There is perhaps a real parallel here between urban social structure and the characteristics of the scientific community of the future, with the "better" classes living well away from the center of the city and taking an interest in its affairs—sometimes too late—only when matters there directly concern their interests or when they are motivated by a sense of *noblesse oblige*. There will thus come, even more clearly, to be two types of "success" within science, two distinct ladders of mobility that are connected only at the bottom, at the university level where all receive their training, and at the top, where those most successful in both basic and applied work will together constitute the elites of the major professional organizations.

So far as social structure is concerned, then, we may expect that in the future the scientific community will come to resemble more and more the engineering profession of today, with a large number of unconnected specialties constituting its major components, the pre-eminence of applied work taken for granted, and the symbols of professional success being allocated more commonly on the basis of practical achievement than in return for basic contributions to a generalized and integrated body of knowledge. But just as there are small groups of theoretical, or "blue-sky," engineers at work today, so there will continue to be comparable groups of basic scientists, relatively isolated from the main community but still highly valued by it. They will be located largely in the universities, and because of their responsibility for training new members of the community, they will continue to hold a highly respected position within the social structure, even if they cease to be so influential in shaping it.

Up to this point I have dealt mainly with future changes in the social structure of science rather than in its normative structure. I do think that the normative structure will come under greater strain as the social organization of science changes, but that this will not result in its being ruptured and then disappearing. As a general rule we may assume that the members of an organization who are in the weaker position in terms of a given issue will be the ones who must make the major adjustments when conflict between their interests and those of the members in the stronger position is clearly recognized. Thus, in the sense that the social structure of science is shaped to accommodate the needs of the majority of its members, it will be the minority of basic scientists, mainly those in academia, who are faced most directly with the need to compromise or adjust their modes of behavior when the dominant structure clearly begins to serve other interests rather than their own. But when the problem lies in the normative structure, where the basic scientists clearly have greater "power" even though they constitute a numerical minority within the community, it will be the applied scientists who must somehow resolve the conflict between the traditional norms of science as they are supported by the community's elite, and their need for a set of norms more appropriate to their own situation.

The traditional norms will continue to be supported not only within the basic research "suburbs" of the scientific metropolis but also throughout the entire metropolis because the prestige of these groups will make the norms important to it. However, the conditions under which the majority of scientists, those in applied research, must work will make the implementation of these norms more and more difficult for them, and the major conflict over norms will be felt by them rather than by the basic scientists. As a result, I would expect that a means will be developed by which a different set of norms more appropriate to the situations in which they are working may be legitimated for these scientists. The new normative structure, perhaps subsidiary to but still capable of existing side by side with the traditional one, will probably be similar to the professional ethics now characteristic of the legal and medical professions; it will focus more upon the attitudes appropriate to the application of specialized knowledge and less upon the ultimate value of the knowledge itself.

To accomplish this, there will come eventually a further

differentiation of the formal social structure itself, so that a man may more clearly know himself and indicate to others to which set of norms he considers himself subject. This will probably come first simply in the firmer establishment of a legitimate and non-invidious distinction between basic and applied research in each major field, just as today "applied mathematics" is distinguished from "pure mathematics," and "applied physics" from both theoretical and experimental "pure" physics. Then the distinction will be supported by the establishment of separate journals designed to meet the needs of each group, and perhaps also by the establishment of different categories of membership or different "sections" within the major organizations that will reflect these distinctions on an organizational basis. Perhaps the history of the American Psychological Association, in which both clinical (applied) and experimental (basic) interests have developed together (rather than originating separately and forming the basis of separate professional societies) may provide some insights into the process through which this may come about.

Summary

The future of the scientific community or, now, the scientific metropolis, will be characterized mainly by a greater differentiation of both its social structure and its normative structure. This will mean that the traditional social system of science must "move over" to some extent to make room for the growing and more obviously independent part of science that is directly concerned with the application of scientific knowledge and research techniques to the problems of the larger society. The particular points of conflict that develop will center for the basic scientists upon the nature of their participation in the social structure of science and for the applied scientists upon the nature of the normative structure that is supposed to guide their activities. The main outlines of the scientific metropolis will resemble more closely those of the engineering profession of today rather than the smaller, "purely" scientific societies of previous decades. The norms and values characteristic of these societies, however, will continue to represent the ideals of the metropolis, even though they may be honored more in theory than in actual practice by most; and there will develop large groups within science who feel honestly and rightly that these standards are not applicable to their work. Instead, these groups will make up the part of the scientific metropolis which resembles more closely the service professions than the academic profession.

Hagstrom suggests that neither "a prediction that the spirit of science will decline while its forms continue to expand," nor "a prediction that science may become the province of specialized cults that will be irresponsible from the perspective of the larger community"[12] is likely to be true. I am in essential agreement with him on this point—and may be in some disagreement with an earlier published statement of my own on this question[13]—and hope that my attempt to characterize the nature of the social system of science in the future may represent a step toward our understanding of the specific ways in which "the tension between professional autonomy and the control of professions leads to the development of organizational forms that can accommodate both."[14]

Postscript

It is certainly not a sociologist's most impressive demonstration of his faith in a theory when the principal test he proposes for it is a fairly vague set of predictions about the state of things some thirty years in the future. Yet I have been unable to discover any more appropriate way to "test" the explanatory adequacy of the model presented here; for the time being, its value will have to be determined by the reader's sense of its logical consistency and meaningfulness, and, later, by the extent to which it provokes fruitful argument and research.

I have tried to develop, in at least embryonic form, a model of major social institutions—social systems—so that the basic dynamics of the social system of science may be both more clearly understood and more directly related to the study of other social phenomena. This has involved a sort of reductionism, at least in assuming that it is important for us to pay attention to *why* people want to do what we sociologists think their groups *need* them to do if these groups are to continue their corporate existence. My own feeling, obviously, is that I have been able to make some headway in linking motivational structures and normative structures in such a way that the forces making science "go" in the directions that it "goes" can be better appreciated. Hoist most appropriately by my own petard, however, I must admit that I am incompetent to render a final decision on the matter. Regardless of the value of this work, then, I can only admit to having had a great deal of pleasure in *trying* to be creative, to further our understanding of social phenomena in general and of the social system of science in particular. No scientist, I think, can really say more than this.

Footnotes for Chapter 7

1. This chapter draws heavily, but with some modification, on my article, "The Coming Changes in American Science," *Science*, vol. 142, no. 3591, pp. 464–467.
2. Lawrence S. Kubie, "Some Unsolved Problems of the Scientific Career," reprinted from the American Scientist, vol. 42 (1954), pp. 104–112, in Barber and Hirsch, p. 222.
3. "Science—Report to the Board of Directors, AAAS," *AAAS Bulletin*, June 1965.
4. Much of the material in this section is taken from my paper, " 'The Literature' of Science and the Publication Explosion," presented at the annual meetings of the American Sociological Association in Montreal, September, 1964.
5. Philip H. Abelson, "Science Reporting," *Science*, vol. 139, no. 3551, p. 177.
6. See Hagstrom, pp. 93–94, for a discussion of this incident from another point of view.
7. Abelson, *op. cit.*
8. Pitirim A. Sorokin, *Fads and Foibles in Modern Sociology and Related Sciences* (Chicago: Henry Regnery, 1956), pp. 196 and 343.
9. Alvin M. Weinberg, "Scientific Communication," *International Science and Technology* (April 1963), p. 71.
10. Project on Scientific Information Exchange in Psychology, William D. Garvey, Director, "The Role of the Technical Report in the Dissemination of Scientific Information," APA-PSIED Report 13 (Washington, D.C.: American Psychological Association, April 1965), p. 208.
11. Anselm Strauss and Lee Rainwater, with Marc J. Swartz and Barbara G. Berger, *The Professional Scientist: A Study of American Chemists* (Chicago: Aldine, 1962), pp. 188–189. This study is particularly useful as an analysis of a scientific specialty undergoing the process of "professionalization" today.
12. Hagstrom, p. 296.
13. Storer, "The Coming Changes in American Science."
14. Hagstrom, p. 296.

Selected Bibliography

Abelson, Philip H., "Science Reporting," *Science,* vol. 139, no. 3551, p. 177.

Allport, Floyd H., *Theories of Perception and the Concept of Structure.* New York: Wylie, 1955.

Anderson, H. H. (ed.), *Creativity and Its Cultivation.* New York: Harper & Row, Publishers, 1959.

Back, Kurt H., "The Behavior of Scientists: Communication and Creativity," *Sociological Inquiry,* vol. 32 (Winter 1962), pp. 82–87.

Barber, Bernard, *Science and the Social Order.* New York: Free Press, 1952.

——, "Sociology of Knowledge and Science," in Hans L. Zetterberg (ed.), *Sociology in the United States of America: A Trend Report.* Paris: UNESCO, 1956, pp. 68–70. (a)

——, "Sociology of Science: A Trend Report and Bibliography," *Current Sociology,* vol. 5 (1956), pp. 91–153. (b)

——, and Walter Hirsch (eds.), *The Sociology of Science.* New York: Free Press, 1962.

Barnes, Louis B., *Organizational Systems and Engineering Groups: A Comparative Study of Two Technical Groups in Industry.* Boston: Division of Research, Harvard Business School, 1960.

Barron, Frank, *Creativity and Psychological Health.* Princeton, N.J.: Van Nostrand, 1963.

——, "The Psychology of Creativity," in *New Directions in Psychology, II.* New York: Holt, Rinehart and Winston, 1965.

Bello, Francis, "The Young Scientists," in The Editors of *Fortune*, *The Mighty Force of Research*. New York: McGraw-Hill, 1956, pp. 21–39.

Ben-David, Joseph, "Roles and Innovations in Medicine," *American Journal of Sociology*, vol. 65 (1960), pp. 557–568. (a)

——, "Scientific Productivity and Academic Organization in Nineteenth Century Medicine," *American Sociological Review*, vol. 25 (1960), pp. 828–843. (b)

——, "Scientific Endeavor in Israel and the United States," *The American Behavioral Scientist*, vol. 6, no. 4 (1962), pp. 12–16.

——, "Scientific Growth: A Sociological View," *Minerva* (Summer 1964), pp. 455–476.

Bennis, Warren G., "The Effect of Academic Goods on Their Market," *American Journal of Sociology*, vol. 62 (1956), pp. 28–33. (a)

——, "Some Barriers to Teamwork in Social Research," *Social Problems*, vol. 3 (1956), pp. 223–235. (b)

——, "Values and Organization in a University Social Research Group," *American Sociological Review*, vol. 21 (1956), pp. 555–563. (c)

Blau, Peter M., *Exchange and Power in Social Life*. New York: Wiley, 1964.

Brown, Paula, "Bureaucracy in a Government Laboratory," *Social Forces*, vol. 32 (1954), pp. 259–268.

Coler, Myron A. (ed.) *Essays on Creativity in the Sciences*. New York: New York University Press, 1963.

Collette, Patricia, *Undergraduate Mathematics Teaching: Settings and Staff*. Chicago: University of Chicago National Opinion Research Center, Report 94, October 1963.

Cooley, William W., *Career Development of Scientists: An Overlapping Longitudinal Study*. Cambridge, Mass.: Graduate School of Education, Harvard University, 1963.

Crane, Diana, "Scientists at Major and Minor Universities: A Study of Productivity and Recognition," *American Sociological Review*, vol. 30, no. 5 (1965), pp. 699–714.

Davis, Kingsley, "Prostitution," in Merton, Robert K. and Robert A. Nisbet (eds.), *Contemporary Social Problems*. New York: Harcourt, 1961.

Dedijer, Stefan, "Research and Freedom in Undeveloped Countries," *Bulletin of the Atomic Scientists*, vol. 13 (1957), pp. 238–242.

——, "Why Did Daedalus Leave?," *Science*, vol. 133 (1961), pp. 2047–2052.

———, "Measuring the Growth of Science," *Science,* vol. 138 (1962), pp. 781–788.

DeWitt, Nicholas, "Soviet Science: The Institutional Debate," *Bulletin of the Atomic Scientists,* vol. 16 (1960), pp. 208–211.

———, *Education and Professional Employment in the U.S.S.R.* Washington, D.C.: National Science Foundation, 1961.

———, "Politics of Soviet Science," *The American Behavioral Scientist,* vol. 6, no. 4 (1962), pp. 7–11.

Dupre, J. Stefan, and Sanford A. Lakoff, *Science and the Nation.* Englewood Cliffs, N.J.: Prentice-Hall, 1962.

Dupree, A. Hunter, *Science in the Federal Government: A History of Politics and Activities to 1940.* Cambridge, Mass.: Harvard University Press, 1957.

Durkheim, Emile, *The Elementary Forms of the Religious Life* (J. W. Swain, transl.). New York: Crowell Collier and Macmillan, Inc., 1961.

Eiduson, Bernice T., *Scientists: Their Psychological World.* New York: Basic Books, 1962.

Garfield, Eugene, Irving H. Sher, and Richard J. Torpie, *The Use of Citation Data in Writing the History of Science.* Philadelphia: Institute for Scientific Information, Inc., 1964.

Garvey, William D., director, *Project on Scientific Information Exchange in Psychology,* vol. 1, Reports 1–9. Washington, D.C.: American Psychological Association, 1963.

———, *The Role of the Technical Report in the Dissemination of Scientific Information.* Washington, D.C.: American Psychological Association, April 1965.

Gilpin, Robert, *American Scientists and Nuclear Weapons Policy.* Princeton, N.J.: Princeton University Press, 1962.

———, and Christopher Wright (eds.), *Scientists and National Policy-Making.* New York: Columbia University Press, 1964.

Ghiselin, Brewster (ed.), *The Creative Process.* New York: New American Library, 1955.

Glaser, Barney G., *Organizational Scientists: Their Professional Careers.* Indianapolis: Bobbs-Merrill, 1964.

———, " 'Differential Association and the Institutional Motivation of Scientists," *Administrative Science Quarterly,* vol. 10, no. 1 (June 1965), pp. 82–97.

Goode, William J., *The Family.* "Foundations of Modern Sociology Series," Alex Inkeles (ed.). Englewood Cliffs, N.J.: Prentice-Hall, 1964.

Gordon, Gerald, Sue Marquis, and O. W. Anderson, "Freedom

and Control in Four Types of Scientific Settings," *The American Behavioral Scientist,* vol. 6, no. 4 (1962), pp. 39–42.

Gouldner, Alvin W., "Reciprocity and Autonomy in Functional Theory," in Llewellyn Gross (ed.), *Symposium on Sociological Theory.* Evanston, Ill.: Harper & Row, Publishers, 1959, pp. 241–270.

——, "The Norm of Reciprocity," *American Sociological Review,* vol. 25 (1960), pp. 161–178.

Grazia, Alfred de, (ed.), "The Politics of Science and Dr. Velikovsky," *The American Behavioral Scientist,* vol. 7, no. 1 (September 1963), entire issue.

Gruenberger, F. J., "A Measure for Crackpots," *Science,* vol. 145, no. 3639, pp. 1413–1415.

Hagstrom, Warren O., *The Scientific Community,* New York: Basic Books, 1965.

Hall, A. R., "Merton Revisited," *History of Science,* vol. 2 (1963), pp. 1–16.

Heilbroner, Robert L., *The Making of Economic Society.* Englewood Cliffs, N.J.: Prentice-Hall, 1962.

Hodge, Robert W., Paul M. Siegel, and Peter H. Rossi, "Occupational Prestige in the United States, 1925–1963," *American Journal of Sociology,* vol. 70 (November 1964), pp. 286–302.

Kaplan, Norman, "Research Atmospheres in Two Different Institutional Contexts," paper read at the annual meeting of the American Sociological Association, Chicago, 1959. (a)

——, "The Role of the Research Administrator," *Administrative Science Quarterly,* vol. 4 (1959), pp. 20–42. (b)

——, "The Western European Scientific Establishment in Transition," *The American Behavioral Scientist,* vol. 6, no. 4 (1962), pp. 17–21.

——, "The Relation of Creativity to Sociological Variables in Research Organization," in C. W. Taylor and F. Barron (eds.), *Scientific Creativity: Its Recognition and Development.* New York: Wiley, 1963.

——, "The Sociology of Science," in Robert E. Faris, (ed.), *Handbook of Modern Sociology.* Chicago: Rand McNally, 1964.

——, "Professional Scientists in Industry: An Essay Review," *Social Problems,* vol. 13, no. 1 (Summer 1965), pp. 88–97. (a)

——, (ed.), *Science and Society.* Chicago: Rand McNally, 1965, (b)

Kidd, Charles V., "Basic Research—Description versus Definition," *Science,* vol. 129, no. 3346, (1959), pp. 368–371.
Knapp, R. H., and H. B. Goodrich, *Origins of American Scientists.* Chicago: University of Chicago Press, 1952.
———, and J. J. Greenbaum, *The Younger American Scholar.* Chicago: University of Chicago Press, 1953.
Kornhauser, William, *Scientists in Industry.* Berkeley: University of California Press, 1962.
Krohn, Roger G., "Science and Social Change: The Effects of New Institutional Locales on the Traditional Structure of Science" (unpublished doctoral dissertation, University of Minnesota, 1960).
———, "The Institutional Location of the Scientist and His Scientific Values," *IRE Transactions on Engineering Management,* EM-8, no. 3 (September 1961), pp. 133–138.
Kubie, Lawrence S., "Some Unsolved Problems of the Scientific Career," *American Scientist,* vol. 42 (1954), pp. 104–112.
Kuhn, Alfred, *The Study of Society: A Unified Approach.* Homewood, Illinois: The Dorsey Press, 1963.
Kuhn, Thomas S., *The Structure of Scientific Revolutions.* Chicago: University of Chicago Press, 1962.
Lamson, Robert, "Scientists and Congressmen" (unpublished doctoral dissertation, University of Chicago, 1960).
Loomis, Charles P., *Social Systems: Essays on Their Persistence and Change.* Princeton, N.J.: Van Nostrand, 1960.
Marcson, Simon, "Role Adaptation of Scientists in Industrial Research," *IRE Transactions on Engineering Management,* EM-7 (1960), pp. 159–166. (a)
———, *The Scientist in American Industry.* Princeton, N.J.: Industrial Relations Section, Princeton University, 1960. (b)
Mauss, Marcel, *The Gift.* New York: Free Press, 1954.
Meier, Richard L., "Research as a Social Process: Social Status, Specialism, and Technical Advance in Great Britain," *British Journal of Sociology,* vol. 2, no. 1 (March 1951), pp. 91–104.
Meltzer, Leo, "Scientific Productivity and Organizational Settings," *Journal of Social Issues,* vol. 12 (1956), pp. 32–40.
Menzel, Herbert, *The Flow of Information Among Scientists: Problems, Opportunities, and Research Questions.* New York: Columbia University Bureau of Applied Social Research, 1958 (mimeo).
———, *Review of Studies in the Flow of Information among*

Scientists. New York: Columbia University Bureau of Applied Social Research, 1958. 2 vols (mimeo).

Merton, Robert K., "Science, Technology, and Society in Seventeenth-Century England," *Osiris* (Bruges, Belgium), vol. 4 (1938), pp. 360–632.

——, *Social Theory and Social Structure*, rev. ed. New York: Free Press, 1957. (a)

——, "Priorities in Scientific Discovery: A Chapter in the Sociology of Science," *American Sociological Review*, vol. 22, no. 6 (December 1957), pp. 635–659. Reprinted in Barber and Hirsch (1962). (b)

——, "Singletons and Multiples in Scientific Discovery: A Chapter in the Sociology of Science," *Proceedings of the American Philosophical Society*, vol. 105, no. 5 (October 1961), pp. 470–486.

——, "The Ambivalence of Scientists," *Bulletin of the Johns Hopkins Hospital*, vol. 112 (1963), pp. 77–97. (a)

——, "Resistance to the Systematic Study of Multiple Discoveries in Science," *European Journal of Sociology*, vol. 4 (1963), pp. 237–282. (b)

Merz, Louise E., "The Graduate School as a Socializing Agency: A Pilot Study of Sociological Aspects of Graduate Training in the Physical Sciences" (unpublished doctoral dissertation, Cornell University, 1961).

National Science Foundation, *American Science Manpower, 1962* (NSF 64–16). Washington, D.C.: Government Printing Office, 1964.

——, "Salaries and Professional Characteristics of U. S. Scientists, 1964," *Reviews of Data on Science Resources*, vol. 1, no. 2 (December 1964).

Obler, Paul C., and Herman A. Estrin (eds.), *The New Scientist*. New York: Doubleday, 1962.

Parsons, Talcott, *The Structure of Social Action*. New York: McGraw-Hill, 1937.

——, *The Social System*. New York: Free Press, 1951.

——, "On the Concept of Power," *Proceedings of the American Philosophical Society*, vol. 107, no. 3 (1963), pp. 232–262.

——, "On the Concept of Influence," *Public Opinion Quarterly*, vol. 27 (Spring 1963), pp. 38–51.

——, and Storer, Norman W., "The Disciplines as a Differentiating Force," in Dan Bergen (ed.), *Symposium on the Foundations of Access to Knowledge*. Syracuse: Syracuse University Press, 1966.

Pelz, Donald C., G. D. Mellinger, and R. C. Davis, *Human Relations in a Research Organization*. Ann Arbor: University of Michigan, Institute for Social Research, 1953. 2 vols. (mimeo).

————, "Some Social Factors Related to Performance in a Research Organization," *Administrative Science Quarterly*, vol. 1 (1956), pp. 310–325.

————, "Interaction and Attitudes Between Scientists and the Auxiliary Staff: I. Viewpoint of the Staff; II. Viewpoint of the Scientists," *Administrative Science Quarterly*, vol. 4 (1959), pp. 321–336, 410–425.

————, "Organizational Atmosphere, Motivation, and Research Contribution," *The American Behavioral Scientist*, vol. 6, no. 4 (1962), pp. 43–47.

————, "Motivation of the Engineering and Research Specialist," American Management Association, *General Management Series*, no. 186 (no date), pp. 36–42.

Perry, Stewart, E., Social Processes in Psychiatric Research: A Study in the Sociology of Science (Harvard University: unpublished doctoral dissertation, 1963).

Price, Derek J. de Solla, *Little Science, Big Science.* New York: Columbia University Press, 1963.

Price, Don K., *Government and Science: Their Dynamic Relation in American Democracy.* New York: New York University Press, 1954.

————, "The Scientific Establishment," *Proceedings of the American Philosophical Society*, vol. 106, no. 3 (June 1962), pp. 235–245.

————, *The Scientific Estate.* Cambridge, Mass.: Harvard University Press, 1965.

Roe, Anne, *The Making of a Scientist.* New York: Dodd, Mead, 1953.

Rogers, Harold, "Pianist Explains Power of Music Emotion: An Interview with Byron Janis," *Christian Science Monitor*, December 9, 1964, p. 13.

Shepard, Herbert A., "Basic Research in the Social System of Pure Science," *Philosophy of Science*, vol. 23, no. 1 (January 1956), pp. 48–57.

Shilling, Charles W., *Informational Communication Among Bioscientists, I.* Washington, D.C.: George Washington University Biological Sciences Communication Project, December 1963 (mimeo); vol. II, 1964 (mimeo).

Snow, C. P., *The Search.* New York: New American Library, 1960.

Sorokin, Pitirim A., *Fads and Foibles in Modern Sociology and Related Sciences.* Chicago: Regnery, 1956.

Stein, M. I., and Shirley J. Heinze, *Creativity and the Individual:*

Summaries of Selected Literature in Psychology and Psychiatry. New York: Free Press, 1960.

Storer, Norman W., "Science and Scientists in an Agricultural Research Organization: A Sociological Study" (unpublished dissertation, Cornell University, 1961).

——, "Research Orientations and Attitudes toward Teamwork," *IRE Transactions on Engineering Management, EM-9,* (March 1962), pp. 29–33. (a)

——, "Some Sociological Aspects of Federal Science Policy," *The American Behavioral Scientist,* vol. 6, no. 4 (December 1962), pp. 27–30. (b)

——, "The Coming Changes in American Science," *Science,* vol. 142, no. 3591 (October 25, 1963), pp. 464–467.

——, " 'The Literature' of Science and the Publication Explosion." Paper presented at the annual meetings of the American Sociological Association, Montreal, September 1964.

——, "Basic Versus Applied Research: The Conflict Between Means and Ends in Science," *Indian Sociological Bulletin,* vol. 2, no. 1 (October 1964), pp. 34–42.

Strauss, Anselm L., and Lee Rainwater, *The Professional Scientist: A Study of American Chemists.* Chicago: Aldine, 1962.

Taylor, C. W., and F. Barron (eds.), *Scientific Creativity: Its Recognition and Development.* New York: Wiley, 1963.

West, S. Stewart, "The Ideology of Academic Scientists," *IRE Transactions on Engineering Management, EM-7* (1960), pp. 54–62.

——, "Sibling Configurations of Scientists," *American Journal of Sociology,* vol. 66, no. 3 (1960), pp. 268–274. (b)

Weinberg, Alvin M., "Scientific Communication," *International Science and Technology* (April 1963), pp. 65–74.

White, Robert W., "Motivation Reconsidered: The Concept of Competence," *Psychological Review,* vol. 66 (1959), pp. 297–331.

Wilson, Logan, *The Academic Man.* New York: Oxford University Press, 1942.

Wolfle, Dael, *Science and Public Policy.* Lincoln, Nebraska: University of Nebraska Press, 1959.

Znaniecki, Florian, *The Social Role of the Man of Knowledge.* New York: Columbia University Press, 1940.

Index